A Dynamic Theory of Communication

A Dynamic Theory
of Communication

Orlando Gomes

Nova Science Publishers, Inc.
New York

LIBRARY OF CONGRESS CATALOGING-IN-PUBLICATION DATA

Gomes, Orlando, 1964-
  A dynamic theory of communication / Orlando Gomes.
      p. cm.
  Includes bibliographical references and index.
  ISBN 978-1-60741-341-7
  1. Communication. 2. Communication--Economic aspects. I. Title.
  P90.G527 2009
  302.201--dc22
                           2009008015

Published by Nova Science Publishers, Inc. ✦ *New York*

CONTENTS

INTRODUCTORY NOTE

Communication is a dynamic and complex process. It is essentially with this fact that the following five chapters are concerned with.

The study of human communication introduces us in a world of multiple scenarios, agents, variables and interconnections, which are important to understand. As in any scientific discipline, the compromise between abstraction and a rigorous analysis, on one hand, and the need to discuss subjects in all their complexity and deepness, on the other hand, is a difficult task, and some simplifications and shortcomings become inevitable. In the analysis of such a wide and pervasive subject as it is communication, it is necessary to choose a path, to define strategies of analysis and to formulate concrete problems.

In this book, communication is worked on the basis of mathematical models that deal with relations between variables of the communicational process. Centering the attention on the notion of dynamic process, techniques of intertemporal analysis and optimal control are considered with the goal of highlighting and reinforcing some of the main ideas that the communication theory has produced and explored in the last few decades.

Basically, nothing of truly new is revealed about the process of communication. It is referred that this is much more than a simple process of sending and receiving messages, the emphasis is placed on the notion of interaction and some variations of the process as the result of the context and of the used media are explored. The above topics constitute the foundations of today's communication theory.

The main distinction between this and other approaches consists on the set of tools used in the analysis. Having in mind the extreme difficulty that the modelling of human behavior implies, the built problems allow to emphasize the role of the main variables of the communication process and the way in which these might be related; this is done by resorting to a dynamic scenario, where choices, capabilities and skills of the individuals are often subject to changes.

The text is organized in five chapters. The first undertakes a survey of the literature on the theory of communication; it refers the conceptual evolution from the linear model sender-receiver to the notion of symbolic interaction, it discusses the contents of communication namely in what concerns the message, its functions and the effectiveness on the transmission process; it also highlights the different types of communication in what respects the context in which it occurs and the channels through which it circulates.

Chapter 2 introduces a first model where communication is directly associated to the choice process; in face of a given circumstance, an individual has to take a decision, attributing probabilities to the various options that are available. These probabilities depend on an implicit process of communication, from which one withdraws two variables that are essential for the decision process: the capacity of choice and a parameter of memory loss or entropy. These two variables work in opposite directions in what concerns the degree of certainty with which choices are made. It is essential to stress that the choice does not occur in an isolated environment, and therefore a structure of social interaction is conceived.

Chapter 2 gives a first framing to the relation between communicational entities, but it neglects an important issue: nothing is said about communicational efficiency; agents make choices based in parameters of learning entropy that they do not control. In reality, individuals will have some control over some of the communication variables and they can use such control to try to optimize the obtained results. In chapter 3 the possibility of choice by a given representative agent is dealt with in a setting of interactive options and weighting of decisions.

Having in mind that cognitive resources are scarce and that individuals cannot apply simultaneously these resources on the process of communication / interaction and on the self awareness necessary to take decisions, they will have to undergo an important process of choice in the intertemporal allocation of the corresponding cognitive resources. In this sense, the communicational efficiency should be understood as the result of an option by the agents between communicating / interacting more or less, knowing that resources are also necessary to manage contents that are gathered from the process of symbolic interaction with third parties.

Chapter 4 abandons the scenario of interpersonal communication that the chapters 2 and 3 implicitly have assumed, to discuss the issue of corporate communication. Once again, the assumed structure of analysis is a dynamic structure, where we consider a problem of intertemporal maximization. The fundamental element of the analysis has its source on the idea that communication in firms is oriented to a specific and well defined end. This goal is profit maximization.

Firms exist to maximize profits (the difference between revenues and costs of production). In this way, communication, as any other resource available to the firm, must be oriented to the fulfilment of the specified goal. Communication can, in this way, be looked at as an investment, that nevertheless has its own peculiarities relatively to other forms of investment of the firm.

Investment in communication allows for the accumulation of a specific form of capital: organizational capital. This has peculiar features relatively to other forms of capital that the firm possesses. Organizational capital is intrinsic to the firm's activity and it is translated on a specific language that does not contribute directly to the generation of income but allows stimulating the working capabilities associated to the human capital input.

Finally, chapter 5 discusses the organization of the economic system in face of the social changes introduced by the new technologies of information and communication. Despite the fact that in structural terms the economic system is facing today the same type of problems that always existed, the new economy involves progressively more the production, transaction and consumption of goods and services with specific characteristics, goods and services that we will designate by digital goods. The main specificity is that digital goods have properties of communication goods, i.e., they can be often thought as contents of communication processes.

Chapter 1

CONCEPTS AND RELATIONS BETWEEN VARIABLES

The most basic interpretation one may adopt about the communication process consists in what Heath and Bryant (2000) designate as the 'paradigm of the hypodermic needle'. According to this notion, communication is the way in which some sender encodes a message and sends it through a given medium or channel to a receiver, who in principle is a priori known from the sender, and who has the function of decoding the message. The communication process will be as much efficient or well succeeded as the receiver changes its behavior (or not) as a function of the received message, in the way intended by the sender.

This is a mechanicist view of the communication process, where the roles of the players (*sender* and *receiver*) are defined at the starting point, and where a series of variables emerges each one playing a well specified and non ambiguous role. These variables are the *message* – the information or the content that is somehow codified and transmitted; the *channel*, through which the message goes from one to the other of the protagonists of a communication process (this is some mean of transmission of messages, that might display a higher or lower degree of sophistication); the *noise,* that is, what obstructs the total efficiency of the communication act (where efficiency is understood as making the message to arrive to the receiver exactly as it was planned by the sender); and the *feedback*, that is, the possibility of the receiver in transmitting back to the one that encodes the message that she has received it and that somehow she has understood it.

The 'hypodermic needle paradigm' is extremely useful for the understanding of what communication truly is. It is, under this perspective, a process of transmission of a message, where it is possible to identify the involved agents and the key variables in order to conclude about the success of the process. It is, however, also a too strict and limited view. It describes not a process but an act; in other words, it characterizes a moment of interaction between two or more parties but it is far from embracing the whole of the communicational relation. This is a dynamic and continuous process which, eventually, has not a beginning or an end, and in which the communication agents exchange messages in a framework of stimulus and response.

In the communication process, the variables message, medium, noise and feedback are effectively present; what is absent is the rigid separation between sender and receiver. In every contact between two parties the communication is reciprocal; both parties are simultaneously senders and receivers. Communication is an interaction process: the notion of process furnishes the idea of temporal continuity while the concept of interaction avoids the arbitrary separation of the roles of the agents involved in the communication process.

In the presence of a paradigm of dynamic interaction process, the concept of efficiency loses part of its objectivity. From a process of interaction it is expected to achieve a set of results, but given that now these are the consequence of a strategic process they are hard to measure *a priori*.

An efficient communication does not have to mean that a receiver understands and internalizes exactly what the other agent wants to transmit; instead, efficiency may be measured by understanding the degree of satisfaction that the interaction produces for both sides. Even for an agent that in some circumstance occupies the position of sender this satisfaction does not have to imply a direct perception of a full understanding from the other party. Being relevant the idea of interaction, such satisfaction or utility may increase if the relation between the parties introduces new variables into the communicational process. The process is malleable in the sense that it may shape and modify the initial purpose of the established interaction.

This chapter intends to systematically characterize, in a succinct way, the main concepts and variables involved in the communication process. The fundamental points were referred in the previous paragraphs: in general terms, communication is a dynamic and interactive process, even though, as it is obvious, it changes its features according to the assumed role players, messages to transmit, contexts of interaction, goals to attain and the used channels. In the following sections these features will be the subject of the analysis.

Section 1.1 dissects communication as an isolated act, it makes references to the main concepts involved in this act and it intends to reemphasize the idea expressed in this introduction that the act is only a small component of a general setting that is much more extensive and that constitutes the process of communicational interaction. In this analysis from the act to the process, we call the attention for some of the most relevant references of the communication theory, who helped this field of study to attain the status of scientific knowledge. In section 1.2, the idea of dynamic process is reemphasized, the origins of communication theory are discussed and the scientific character of communication studies is pointed out.

Relatively to section 1.3, this will focus on the message, on the way this is transmitted and on the goals directly attached to such transmission: information exchange, uncertainty reduction, and persuasion (this last notion relates to the way in which communication should serve the purpose of shaping and changing actions and behaviors).

In section 1.4, the problem of the context is approached – the communication can be understood as a chameleon – it changes its colours with the assumed framing. Communication between two friends, between employer and employee, between a speaker and its audience, have evident differences and the characterization of such differences will effectively be the subject of this section. In section 1.4 we also analyze the possible channels through which messages are diffused and it is discussed how the communication process is influenced by the medium that is used to broadcast the message. Finally, section 1.5 presents some conclusions.

1.1. FROM THE ACT TO THE PROCESS

One of the most influential pioneering interpretations of the communication process is the one furnished by Shannon (1948) and Shannon and Weaver (1949). These authors present the basic structure of the model of the 'hypodermic needle', in which there exists an agent whose function is to transmit information, which is collected from a given source, to some destination, where a given receiver decodes or translates it, having this last agent no capacity or interest in reacting critically. The receiver will accept, under this view, the message without questioning its contents.

Under this linear perspective, sender and receiver are clearly identifiable, and this separation of roles will allow attributing to one of the agents the leading role in the relation that is established – in this case, the sender. Who sends the message has collected information, has thought on a strategy to send the message, has chosen a channel, has obeyed to a stimulus or a necessity for sending it. On the other extreme of the communicational act, the receiver will just receive and decode the message, with the result of this reception being largely the result of the capabilities of who has sent the message.

In the linear paradigm of communication, the idea of efficiency arises immediately and naturally. Communication is as much efficient as the closer the understanding of the receiver is from the sense or meaning of what the sender intends to transmit. Given the passive role of the receiver, the obstacles to the efficiency are found mainly in the message sending process, which can be disturbed by noise, and therefore the main concern should be to minimize such noise. To mitigate noise is not an easy task, since this is essentially an element of unpredictability or, in the words of Krippendorff (1975), as a random variable that reduces predictability.

Associated to the idea of noise is the concept of entropy. Entropy, defined by Weiner (1950) as the degree of lack of organization that exists in a given system, produces noise, obstructing a transmission without flaws (and, thus, efficient) of the message. We will return to the notion of entropy in section 1.3 in order to discuss the role of information in the reduction of uncertainty.

The hypodermic point of view is a mechanicist interpretation that separates communication into a series of pieces that, once nicely oiled, optimize the process of transmission and reception of messages. The notion of fidelity is relevant here, in the sense that what is intended is a loyal reproduction of the sent message in the mind of the receiver.

As it is obvious, communication involves much more than the simple understanding of the technical aspects related to the transmission of messages. Even Shannon and Weaver (1949) recognize such evidence, highlighting that besides the optimal transmission of messages, the reflection about communicational interaction should also approach questions of semantic nature. The concern is with how the way in which messages are composed and organized (through words or any other way) has influence over the sending, transmission and reception processes; also, it is relevant the way in which the receiver's behavior is affected and if the changes of behavior are related with the true meaning of the message or, in alternative, with the receiver own idiosyncrasies.

The study of communication gains a new stimulus in the moment in which it leaves the focus on the transmission and it begins to concentrate attention in the forces that influence human interaction. In fact, communication (at least, through words) is an eminently human process, which involves factors that are intrinsic to the human cognition and to the human emotion. Because each individual possesses distinct experiences and cognitive and emotional capacities, every communication process is, in itself, unique.

The communication agents will have different personalities, different values and different life experiences, and these will translate in peculiar behavior that can make it easier or harder the communication for different protagonists and subjects. Factors as the degree of attention evidenced by the receiver or the disagreement relatively to the message that is intended to be transmitted may strongly restrict the impact that is supposed to be attained; such factors are extremely volatile since they are in constant mutation and evolution in the human mind.

The important work of Berlo (1960) popularizes the linear model sender-message-channel-receiver, but simultaneously extends decisively the horizons of the communication science, by recognizing the insufficiencies of such model in face of the complexity of the human interaction.

Following Mead (1934), who has stressed the idea that the essence of communication is the symbolic interaction among individuals, Berlo (1960) has recognized that communication and the individuals personality are interconnected: we communicate in a given way because of what we are, but what we are is also the result of how we communicate. Interpersonal relations and the life in society are built; and the main tool serving such purpose is the communication process or, as these two authors designate it, the 'dynamics of symbolic interaction'.

By making clear that personal, social, economic and political relations have as a key piece the communication process, this should no longer be understood as linear and static. As Schramm (1954, 1973) has highlighted, the ones that communicate are simultaneously senders and receivers – the way a message is received and an answer is given to it (or not) is also a form of communication. In reality, it is impossible not to communicate; any action addressed at a third party emerges in this sense as a form of communication.

Communication relations are more than the relation between a sender and a receiver; communication relations are relations of dynamic interaction and it is in this sense that communication will be understood hereafter: as a continuous process, in permanent mutation, which has no attached pre-defined sequence of actions and where all the elements of the system interact and are mutually affected.

In this way, communication will not even be just a process of dynamic interaction; it will be dynamic interaction in a context of complexity. To translate this complexity to analytical structures is not simple and some compromises relatively to the real world have to be assumed. In the chapters that follow, despite of the assumed simplifying assumptions, we will try to characterize the communication, under an analytical point of view, as a dynamic process and where interaction among agents is evidenced.

Synthesizing, communication is related with a process of encoding, transmission and decoding of messages, a process that on a first approach may be decomposed into a simple group of acts of stimulus and response, but that on a deeper analysis is revealed to be the basis of social interaction, where desires, motivations, needs, expectations, skills and idiosyncrasies of the human being are revealed.

1.2. COMMUNICATION AS A SCIENCE

The hardest task in any field of scientific knowledge consists in defining rigorously and in a few words its object. Communication does not escape to this rule. What is really communication and what does communication theory intend to explain?

In a generic way, the previous section has furnished some clues to answer the posed question. Communication as a science will correspond to the study of human interaction. Any social relation that is established is based on the process of communication; without this, the interaction at all levels, from the interpersonal to the organizational, would be absent.

Even today, various studies in the scientific field of communication emphasize the linear view of sending and receiving messages, as it is the case of Mortensen (1997) and Green (1997). In particular, the first of these authors concentrates attention on the concept of 'miscommunication', arguing that the goal of communication consists in avoiding the failure of the process of communication in what concerns achieving a given objective defined at a starting date. The message should be, in this perspective, strategically planned and carefully transmitted, since the purpose of communication is the clear and coherent transmission of messages; the purpose is to avoid failures and to promote efficiency.

The point in favour of the previous perspective is that it offers a justification for communication as a malleable process, because without receptivity to change, the players in any communicational process would be incapable of avoiding mistakes and to make the required adjustments in order to eliminate communication failures. Nevertheless, as Stewart (1995), Lyne (1998) and Sheperd (1999) highlight, communication is much more than the simple transmission of messages; it is a complex process arising from the merger of two worlds: the one from the sender, who conceives and sends the message, and the one from the receiver, who receives and gives a meaning to it.

Authors as Pearce and Cronen (1980), Rogers and Kincaid (1981) and McLaughlin (1984) support precisely the interpretation that communication is the instrument through which it is possible to create, maintain, change and extinguish social relations and identities. Therefore, studying communication implies the analysis of the way a social order is formed by the contact between individuals and groups of individuals. The social reality can be understood, transmitted and perpetuated through the communication process but, more than this, communication creates social phenomena and imposes a particular order to the way the society works.

In particular, Rogers and Kincaid (1981) give relevance to the idea that communication translates the mutual understanding in social contexts. Social interaction would be, in the analysis of these authors, a cyclical process through which meanings are attributed in order to promote a process of convergence. Here, convergence means that under an interaction process stimulated by communication, the agents involved in the relation will be directed to a common point, i.e., to a point of consensus.

Also Habermas (1981), Bourdieu (1986), Leydesdorff (2000) and Schans (2001) interpret communication as a joint process of interpretation and negotiation, through which goals are chosen and means to attain the goals are selected; in this sense, communication will avoid divergence because it is oriented to consensus. Hirokawa (1990) and Maznevski (1994) suggest that communication will be as much important as the more complex are the problems the agents face, because it will be in such contexts that the point of views will be more divergent, meaning that a larger effort will be needed to integrate perspectives towards convergence. The efficiency of communication is an issue that gains special acuity in contexts of complex interaction and, for this reason, several authors search for ways to define communication paths conducting to quality decisions [see Vennix (1996) and van Ruler (1999)].

Following a same line of reasoning, Habermas (1987) connects the concept of communication to the idea of social nets. These nets, according to the author, are not living organisms, and therefore their reproduction is not guaranteed. Thus, communication requires effort in maintaining an endogenous dynamic process, stimulated by their participants. Nevertheless, communication also has a component of self regeneration, in the sense that it carries many properties and it can generate new ways of interaction that create value in the relation between the involved parties.

To highlight communication as a phenomenon of groups, Kroon, Pierick, Vlieger, Backus and King (2002) mention the concept of social capital. According to these authors, social capital will correspond to the aggregation of potential benefits that originate in the cordiality and the sense of obligation that one person or group has relatively to other persons or groups; as this definition makes clear, the formation of social capital is the result of communication. Only the direct contact that communication allows for can lead to the generation of trust between individuals and of a common language that contributes to accumulate social capital.

Social capital has obvious advantages in what concerns efficiency and in what regards cooperation between different agents, but it can also help to maintain existing non innovative relations and a limited responsiveness to interaction alternatives. The convergence that communication allows promotes the accumulation of social capital, with good and bad consequences.

Following a similar logic, we can state the concept of intellectual capital. Through interaction, knowledge is conceived and in this way communication is also a form of investment in intellectual capital.

The way in which the individuals evaluate their interaction shapes the process of communication; in the same way, through communication, the social reality is built. We observe a mutual mechanism of creation of routines and of effort minimization, that is, we communicate in order to make social relations easier and as these relations are built the process of communication gains routines that simplify interaction; from the moment we know our partner in some relation, it is possible to adopt simplification mechanisms. Once again, the idea of a dynamic process emerges: interaction through communication does not evolve in a random way; this interaction is progressively built and strengthened, gaining a particular and original shape.

Communication needs a scenario or a context. Routines and simplifications arise with a deeper contact, because this contact raises the knowledge both parties. Knowledge, in turn, allows to reduce uncertainty and in this way it is a key variable on the characterization of the communication process.

Having a more or less precise notion of what communication deals with, we can systematize some points that can be understood as the object of study of this scientific field. Communication has, as object of study:

(i) Information transmission. Individuals communicate in order to obtain and interpret information that helps them to reduce uncertainty about the physical and social environment that surrounds them. Therefore, to know how the individuals exchange information in order to be increasingly aware of their own roles in the various groups that they belong to is something vital and a central study element of the communication science;

(ii) Exchange of symbols and meanings. As a social being, the human being interacts symbolically. If we do not learn and understand a large set of symbols and signs that the society shares, we will have difficulty in belonging to groups, and without this belonging feeling life in society becomes impossible. Then, it is evident that the perception of how and with what intentions the human being exchanges meanings is also a central object of analysis of this science;

(iii) Strategic behavior and communication efficiency. Social relations can assume many shapes, however communication frequently translates social competition. We want to communicate well to have success, gain social status and to make others respect and like us. In this perspective, it is important for the communication science to try to understand how each individual or entity places herself / itself in the complex communicational system of the society and how she / it is able to manage the skills of communication in order to, given a set of predefined goals, be the more well succeeded as possible;

(iv) Building individual identities. Society, in its diversity and complexity, gives to the individuals the ability of choosing. Any one of us may try to identify himself with particular groups or to create a unique identity with respect to others. Communication oriented to the formation of personality and to the acquisition of determined cultural traces is also a relevant object of study. Note that in this perspective the receiver eventually gains a central role in the communication process: the central point is not a sender trying to make is message reach a given group of receivers but an agent that searches in a conscious way to be the receiver of the available messages that are the most convenient in order for the agent to gain the identity that is desired. In today's society, in which the available messages exist in a large number and they come from a large set of sources it is evident this increasing power of the receiver, which effectively comes from the significant increase of the available options.

Heath and Bryant (2000) identify, besides the scientific object, also the origins of the communication theory. According to these authors, the communication theory is the result of uniting four important traditions. The first relevant contribution is the one characterized in the previous section, i.e., the need to understand the transmission and receiving mechanisms of messages. We have already highlighted the relevance of efficiency and quality in the transmission of messages, without which the act of communication would be compromised; however, as it is evident, communication theory was not built solely based on the foundations of systems engineering. The second relevant contribution is the one of social sciences; also as already stated, the development of interpersonal relationships and the perception of the dynamics of social groups are unavoidable elements for the characterization of communication processes. The symbolic interaction is the genesis of the social relations but it is also the seed that the communication allows to germinate.

The remaining two fundamental contributions are the ones provided by linguistics and rhetoric and by the study of the impact of the messages transmitted by the mass media. In what concerns linguistics and rhetoric analysis, it is evident the need that the theory has of explaining the persuasive impact of communication and the corresponding social influence. Each one of us interacts through communication with an objective, which is the one of convincing (or to be convinced of) third parties about something. Thus, the understanding of which are the factors that help in achieving an improved capacity to transmit messages and to persuade the others to act in a certain direction, is crucial to communication. The way in which the rhetoric capacity can be perfected and how the contents of the message can be improved is a fundamental subject of study.

Finally, as the modern society has changed into a mass society in which communication media have taken a universal dimension, it became essential the understanding of how the communication mass media can influence individuals and even create, eventually, a collective awareness. Political propaganda, commercial and institutional advertising, the marketing at the level of the firm, are all phenomena allowed by these media with enormous capabilities. It is also evident that from the moment these media have gained a special relevance in our lives, they become also an important theme of discussion for the communication science; despite the difference in scale and in the used means to get messages through, propaganda, advertising or marketing are forms of communication, i.e., forms of transmitting messages in a context of social interaction.

In an attempt to better understand what communication theory really is, we end up in a crossroad where four paths meet: engineering, social sciences, rhetoric and advertising and propaganda studies.

Communication has also a relevant link with the economic theory. Economics studies the efficient allocation of resources and the way in which costs and benefits are weighted in order to take decisions. Any choice that arises from evaluating costs and benefits can be interpreted as an economic decision. In this perspective, to communicate is synonymous of taking economic decisions.

Communication is a process through which multiple decisions are taken: about how, where, when, and by what means to communicate. Any decision at this level arises from a set of options or choices, and therefore, truly from the evaluation and measurement of the costs involved and of the potentially expected benefits. Communicating consists in negotiating relations and in adopting strategies that maximize some objective function. For example, if we think that the objective of communication is to understand and to be understood, when someone decides to interact with others she will do it only if, according to her evaluation criteria, the cost involved in the effort to be understood is lower than the benefit that is expected from getting the intended message to the receiver with the intended meaning.

The economic perspective of communication implicitly assumes that the agents are rational, i.e., that in each moment of time they are capable of evaluating the available options and to make the right decision. Evidently the human mind cannot be conceived under such strict rationality requirements. Many times, the human communication is intuitive and automatic, obeys to routines and does not arise after an exhaustive process of evaluation of costs and benefits.

As Simon (1955, 1959, 1982) has stressed, the human rationality is limited. Under a scenario of 'bounded rationality' the individuals when confronted with similar choices in different moments of time (or when two individuals are confronted with the same choice, for instance) they can take different decisions, what goes against the rational choice paradigm that the economic science traditionally uses.

Therefore, the rational evaluation is an important reference to explain the choices that at the communicational level may be undertaken. However, since it is a process of human interaction, other issues need to be considered: the role of emotions in the evaluation of choices [Romer (2000)]; the relevance of the cognitive effort associated with the selection of alternatives [Gabaix and Laibson (2004)]; or the identification of failures in the cognitive process, that many times lead to a behavior that has more of an intuitive nature than of rationality [Kahneman (2003)].

1.3. THE MESSAGE

In the final part of the previous section we have raised the doubt of communication being a rational process or, on the contrary, if it obeys to stimulus of an emotional or intuitive order. Whether we consider that communication is rational, and therefore attentive and careful, or we interpret a large part of what we transmit to others as an spontaneous process and the reaction that arises naturally to respond to certain stimuli, the truth is that in any circumstance we make choices; therefore, even when impulsive and intuitive, communication is never random: it has an intention or a purpose.

The purpose of communication can be thought in a scale that goes from the process that is scientifically and strategically thought to the decisions of the moment, which are unreflected or emerging from routine and rituals. Each individual, in distinct social circumstances, communicates in multiple ways; facing an exam in school, it is expected a well thought, planned and prepared communication process; between friends, an individual may follow a less strict and more spontaneous form of communication. The way communication is undertaken is directly attached with the goals or the intentions behind the communication action.

Nonetheless, independently of the involved cognitive effort, there is always an intention in communication and this intention is embodied in the message.

The message is the central element of any communication process. According to McQuail (1987), messages are symbolic constructions that have meaning for the agents of the communication process. The message translates the intentions of agents, but many times it is difficult to define or to identify. We can have more than one message according to the interpretation each agent makes of what is transmitted; the message that the sender intends to deliver may not correspond to what is apprehended by the receiver and among different receivers of a same message this can carry multiple interpretations.

The way we interpret the message that is transmitted can be thought under a same logic in which we have classified the approaches to the communication process: in the 'hypodermic interpretation' the message is seen as the contents of some piece of paper that is tied to an arrow an shoot from a sender to a receiver (we can designate this way of perceiving the message as the 'Robin Wood' message); a second interpretation, approached in a stimulus-response process logic, identifies the message with the receiver reaction, i.e., the transmitted message is what the receiver understands and interprets from the contents that were sent to her. Finally, we can think about the message in the dynamic interaction frame: the message is not something that is sent from an agent to another agent but some content that is built and strengthen as the interaction between the players evolves. As Cherry (1978) highlights, a message is not transmitted but shared; it is a component of an interaction process and it gains unique interpretations each time interaction exists.

Independently of the assumed concept of message, there is no doubt that the efficiency in its delivery or in the way it is shared is crucial. We have referred, in section 1.2, that the message can be disturbed by noise and that this noise introduces uncertainty in the process of communication. Thus, even if we consider a broad interpretation of what communication is (i.e., a process of human interaction), it makes sense to minimize the presence of noise.

To minimize noise, another variable assumes a particular relevance: the feedback. This variable, also present in the initial scheme sender-receiver, can be integrated as a part of the process of communication. In this process, the notions of feedback and message exchange are diluted. In a pure version, feedback is the interpretation of a received message, which once sent to the receiver allows to understand if the strategy of the transmission of the message was the appropriate one and if it attains the required goal. In the perspective of interaction, the feedback can be understood as the next message in an interactive communication process that can be roughly thought as a systematic process of messages exchange.

Feedback helps in reducing uncertainty or entropy in a given communication process, working as a correction device that prevents communication from deviating from the objectives that the parties intend to achieve. By interpreting communication as an interaction process, the feedback arises as a recurrent element of the process that helps the involved parties to attain their goals, i.e., helps communication in achieving efficiency.

The message resorts necessarily to some form of language. The language will be a structural element of the communication process. Through it we can organize thoughts, codify messages, transmit meanings and interpret contents. The language involves a two sided process: on one hand, words and symbols allow to present ideas, but, on the other hand, the language corresponds to the thoughts themselves, i.e., the language used to express an idea is most of the times not dissociable from the corresponding meaning.

The language has correspondence on the code that the societies construct and adopt in order to describe the reality and to transmit information, ideas and thoughts. Words and symbols represent things, feelings, actions and situations and in this way we should associate to the concept of message the main tool it resorts to, which is any form of language, more or less elaborated.

Even if the degree of sophistication of the language and signs system that a society is capable of developing is high, it is always questionable whether the communication process is fully autonomous relatively to the existing code system: is the human being capable of communicating exactly what she intends to, or is the transmitted or shared message always constrained by the linguistic signs available in some predetermined context or culture?

Independently of the existing linguistic system being capable of allowing for effective communication, the language is a basic instrument for the management of social relations through the communication process. Without an articulated language, communication fails, in the sense that it becomes incapable of allowing for the exchange of thoughts and information and for the interaction and the establishment of social relations.

Thus, a common language is not only a tool to get access to others and to the information they possess, but it is also an instrument of perception and interpretation of meaning [Berger and Luckmann (1966), Pondy and Mitroff (1979), Nahapiet and Ghoshal (1998)] and a way of generating new knowledge [Nonaka and Takeuchi (1995)].

The degree of social and economic development that humans have achieved is, without any doubt, attachable to the construction and constant improvement of a system of symbols, words and rules of understanding, without which it would be impossible to attribute meanings. Meanings, on the other hand, are not only a straightforward correspondence between words and things, they are consolidated through interaction.

Until now, this section has focused on the notion of message, how it is central for the communication process, what it means in a context of social interaction and how it makes use of the language to acquire meaning. We need to ask, now, which are the fundamental reasons why messages are shared. In the paragraphs that follow, we will essentially identify two reasons for message sharing: the dissemination of information and the attempt to persuade.

In the assumed context, information and persuasion are not mutually exclusive concepts. A message can have both informative and persuasive contents. Moreover, persuasion will hardly be successful if simultaneously there is no information component in the contents of the transmitted message.

The emotional and cognitive distress provoked by uncertainty is the reason why the sharing of information can be considered the fundamental motive to trigger the act of communication or the exchange of messages. The human being does not feel comfortable with uncertainty; to trade information means knowing others, knowing the reality surrounding each one of us, and, probably the most important, it allows for a self-knowledge, that is, it allows to understand the role that the agent plays in the society she belongs to, how the others perceive her and how she can improve her adaptation to the society in which she is integrated.

Hence, communication can be, without exaggeration, defined as the process of sharing information in order to increase certainty relatively to the surrounding environment, with the objective of guaranteeing a better response capacity relatively to challenges of various orders, and particularly to the ones imposed by social interaction.

Nevertheless, we should be careful when associating the notions of communication and information. One and the other are not the same thing: communication is the process, it is the frame needed to make possible messages sharing; information will be, according to the interpretation of Krippendorff (1977), the energy that flows into this process. Information can be received, sent, transformed and even created inside the communication system, but it should not be identified as the system itself.

Since information flows inside the system of human interaction, it will be flexible and its true form will depend on the specific context of interaction that is being considered. For example, it is a fact that the way information is sent and received depends on the cognitive involvement of the agents. If the agents of some communication process have good knowledge about some subject, if they think such subject concerns them directly or if they think it is a relevant subject independently of their direct involvement, then the agents will be more receptive to absorb information on the theme, and therefore they will be more willing to assimilate and interpret what the other party intends to transmit.

Similarly, the information that flows in the communication process can be interpreted in terms of unawareness about some subject. Following Devito (1986), we can remark that information will be something that exists only in the circumstance when uncertainty is experienced. In the absence of uncertainty, the message will not contribute with any information. In this perspective, a communication process will be as much efficient as the larger is the degree of unawareness of the receiver relatively to the contents of the message; if the contents are already known, then the message is redundant and the process of communication becomes completely innocuous.

According to the above reasoning, the quantity of information that is present in a message will always be a relative concept, since it will depend of the extent of doubt or uncertainty that exists in the mind of the receiver and that is revealed when the message reaches its destiny. For example, if we explain to a child how to tie his shoes, this message may carry a high degree of utility because it transmits a piece of information that has not yet been incorporated. If the same message is passed on to an adult person this will be a perfectly innocuous act of communication, since nothing new is in fact passed on to the individual.

Previous arguments are not to be applied in a blind way to all and every circumstance. Many times, when the individuals already possess a large quantity of information about some issue they are willing to receive additional information on the subject, or even the same information in order to reinforce the meaning that is already apprehended. The human being also experiences insecurity and receiving repeatedly the same message may be a way to minimize such insecurity.

In synthesis, the relevance of information to the communication process is founded on the idea that a message is essentially the means through which the ones that communicate furnish and obtain information. Relatively to the meaning, this arises as the interpretation of the information that the message contains, and it will be dependent on the context, on the language used by the agents and on the motivation and skills of the players.

Until now, we have looked at information as a good thing, i.e., information helps to minimize uncertainty. However, as far as the early work of Shannon and Weaver (1949), the communication theorists have learned to look at information as a two-edged knife.

If it is true that a larger quantity of available information contracts the universe of what remains to know, and therefore reduces the uncertainty of the communication process, it is also true that a larger quantity of information is synonymous of a larger number of variables involved in the process, what can turn harder the acts of sending and receiving messages. Additional quantities of information become redundant and lead to noise; this, in turn, contributes to uncertainty and communication inefficiency.

In this perspective, it makes sense to distinguish between 'good' information and 'bad' information: information will be good if it constitutes a way of adding knowledge allowing to make it easier for the agents to exchange messages and meanings. Information will be bad if it is a device leading to the introduction of additional data into the system, diminishing the capacity of choice as it enlarges the possibilities of choice. Facing a larger number of decision possibilities, the uncertainty or unpredictability will grow making the exchange of messages harder and reducing the effectiveness of the interaction processes.

The already mentioned concept of entropy is central to the analysis of the perverse effects of the introduction of additional information in communication processes. Being entropy the degree of disorganization that exists in a given system, it will correspond to the level of uncertainty, randomness or lack of predictability that is associated to a determined interaction process. If this process corresponds to a communication relation then it is easy and straightforward to arrive to an association between entropy and information. In the absence of entropy, we will have a scenario of certainty or predictability, and therefore all the required information is already available; to introduce additional information would mean to add unpredictability to a certainty scenario. In this sense, we can follow Shannon and Weaver

(1949) in stating that a scenario of maximum entropy is a scenario of maximum information availability.

According to the previous interpretation, a wide set of information means a huge potential of choice, implying a contraction of the level of certainty and the communication process becomes entropic or poorly efficient. Three variables are played here in an integrated way: entropy, information and uncertainty. Large availability of information reduces certainty and therefore causes entropy.

According to the previous point of view, the objective of communication should be the design of messages in such a way that the set of possibilities that the receiver has to interpret the contents of such messages is the more limited as possible, in order for uncertainty and ambiguity to be minimized. Therefore, the more likely is the message, the lower will be the degree of associated entropy and the more exiguous will be the transmitted information.

Note that the concept of lowering the entropy level through the contraction of the amount of information is a logical consequence of the 'hypodermic' linear model of communication. Obviously, if we have a sender and a receiver, we want to withdraw from the path between the two all the obstacles in order to make the contents that the sender desires to transmit effectively available to the receiver in the more immaculate form as possible. It is necessary to lower the noise, that causes entropy and makes it harder the interpretation of the receiver, at least in the sense intended by the sender. Additional information implies introducing in the path between the two agents alternative trajectories that place obstacles to the fast and precise transmission of messages. However, if we interpret the process of communication as a process of symbolic interaction in a dynamic context, the ambiguity or the creation of alternative scenarios concerning the interpretation of messages is not necessarily a perverse effect of the communication process that penalizes the level of utility that the agents withdraw from such process.

Human interaction is complex, as we have remarked before, and this essentially means that the circumstances in which communication occurs can carry substantially different realities. If, on one hand, there are situations in which it is obvious that the optimization of the communication is synonymous of efficiency in the objective transmission of some message, in other cases the reality should be looked at differently. In multiple circumstances regarding human interaction adding information can lead to a richer relation, though more complex, i.e., to simplify the process of communication is not always the way to increase the degree of satisfaction or utility withdrawn from the communication process. Very often, it is the more complex interaction relation, that involves more variables and that deals with a larger number of logical reasonings and emotions, the one that offers a higher satisfaction level to the parties; this means that adding information can be advantageous from a utility point of view even if this raises uncertainty. For example, when someone communicates by offering flowers, a process of communication that involves some ambiguity is being initiated; from the point of view of the receiver this act may be interpret in some different ways, but this does not mean that the receiver will lose utility by being unable of giving an immediate an unequivocal meaning to the act. On the contrary, the utility may rise as such ambiguity can serve the purpose of the agents in developing further the communication interaction. The ambiguity in the communication process may be interpreted as a way to open new doors and to explore additional opportunities of interaction that can lead the players of the process to reach an understanding that maximizes the utility of both sides.

Besides information sharing, the exchange of messages has a second fundamental goal, already referred: persuasion. Persuasion can be defined as the use of a message in order to influence the behavior of others. The power of the message in the sense of persuading others can appeal to the reason or to the emotions.

When we talk about persuasion, we are referring to the process of influencing attitudes and behaviors. In this sense, persuasion is intrinsic to the communication process. When communicating we intend to influence attitudes and behaviors. The notion of persuasion apparently puts at the center of the analysis the sender. The one who sends the message is the one that persuades, convinces or influences others. However, the communication process is in fact much more complex than this; in every interaction there is a reciprocal influence, i.e., frequently the agent that in a moment plays the role of receiver wants to be persuaded of something, or instead simply ignores the efforts of the persuading party, or yet offers resistance and attempts to contradict the other agent when there is disagreement. Again, the process is dynamic, i.e., who convinces who in the communication process is not something that has a unique and one sided answer. Throughout the process, the positions change and evolve and the persuasion process becomes necessarily reciprocal.

As referred, the transmission of information and the persuasion are not conflictual. Without sharing information the capacity of shaping attitudes and behaviors becomes significantly constrained. Information is indispensable to transmit knowledge, which in turn will have a persuasive impact that shapes the way the players act. To the concepts of information and persuasion we add three more that are vital to the success of the communication process: knowledge, attitudes and behaviors. With all these concepts we can build a new definition of what communication is: it will be the means by which information is exchanged with the purpose of creating knowledge in order to turn possible to persuade others to change their behaviors through a modification in their attitudes.

The fundamental point regarding the notion of persuasion in the communication process consists in effectively understanding that individuals are not, in any case, passive receivers of messages. Individuals have goals, and they only change attitudes and behaviors if such serves the specified goals. Individuals are not mere puppets of the communication process, i.e., their way of thinking will not be deterministically shaped, in an inevitable way, by external forces. However, these forces are important; the persuasive force of messages helps in building individuals character, even though they want to remain loyal to a specified set of conduct rules that they think are the most correct according to the introspective effort they have made to acquire some kind of beliefs.

Therefore, agents are capable of offering resistance to messages if this matches their interests. The communication agents are able to evidence selective behaviors, which are a function of contexts, circumstances, beliefs and values. The receivers of a same persuasive message will certainly perceive it and interpret it as they choose to do and in distinct ways across individuals.

On the other hand, the resistance to persuasion will have limits. This is true because persuasion is not always evident. It can take subtle forms. When in a given society we behave according to a set of pre-existent social norms we have been, even without recognizing it, persuaded to adopt such set of rules; this can work as an advantage because without incorporating such norms the life in society would be harder and to adapt the behavior to the circumstances would be a more demanding task.

1.4. THE CONTEXT AND THE COMMUNICATION MEDIA

Communication is not independent of the context in which it occurs. The communication relations are developed in different ways between friends, when a work relation is considered or when a teacher intends to transmit knowledge to her students. The relevance of the context is such that it allows for separating the communication science into a group of sub-disciplines. These can be categorized as follows:

- interpersonal communication;
- organizational communication;
- public / mass communication.

The advanced classification is obviously arbitrary. Other types of communication processes, associated to other contexts, can likewise be assumed. As a matter of simplifying the discussion take the three mentioned disciplines; below we characterize them briefly. In the same way as the context, also the means or the channel that is used is an element that defines the communication process. The above mentioned communication forms have correspondence in specific communication media; for this reason, in this chapter we make a simultaneous characterization of the context of communication and of the media it resorts to.

In a generic way, the communication channel can be defined as the means through which the message is sent from an agent to another. In the interpersonal and organizational communication processes the media can be the simple direct verbal contact or some standard technology as the telephone, the fax or the internet. Mass communication, on the other hand, is efficient only if transmitted through mass communication media, as the written press, the radio or the television.

The means is so important to convey the message that it ends up by having a central role in the way the message arrives to its destine and the effect it has over its receiver. McLuhan (1964) has stated that the means is the message, which is supposed to imply that the way the message is apprehended is a direct function of the used channel. Different channels or media that broadcast the same contents transform these contents in completely different things, provoking diverse effects over the attitudes and behavior of agents.

A large part of the discussion throughout this chapter has referred the communication process as involving two or more parties, but these have not been concretized. In the absence of this specification, we can extrapolate that we were referring essentially to an interpersonal communication, in which a interdependency is automatically established and in which the involved agents jointly define the dynamics of the interaction. Each thing each agent does influences not only the other player but also establishes a path, or a set of alternative paths, through which the interaction evolves.

The relations of interpersonal communication can assume different forms; they can be relations of dependence, conflict, symbiosis or exchange, that is, the action of one agent will always be a reaction to a previous action of another agent, and therefore conflict or cooperation relations are the result of stimuli, replies and strategic sequential behaviors. When someone communicates with us in a pleasant way it is natural that the reply comes in the same pleasant format; in the same way, faced with an act of aggressiveness an agent will generate a conflict response.

In the field of interpersonal communication, we should account also for the problematic of communicational competence. The individuals possess distinct cognitive and emotional characteristics, what makes them more or less prepared for specific forms of communication. The study of interpersonal communication must, then, try to perceive a diversity of capabilities and competences that culminate in divergent results for identical contexts and characteristics of the communicational process, given the idiosyncrasies of the considered players.

Life in society requires individuals to be organized in wealth generating entities – firms – and in other types of associations relating politics, culture, sports, religion, among others. The organizations of various types are groups of individuals that pursue a set of activities with a common goal, which corresponds to the mission or the reason for the existence of the organization, but that simultaneously are the stage of particular interests of their members, which can assume contours of rivalry or conflict.

Organizations are, according to the above comment, complex entities that can work only by establishing an efficient net of communication between its members and from its members to the exterior. It is this reality that gives autonomy and relevance to the study of organizational communication.

As it is obvious, a precise study of organizational communication has to be undertaken in the presence of some concrete organization, since these differ in dimension, purpose, working relations, among many other factors. In general traces, it is relevant to understand that the organizational communication analysis should furnish some clues to perceive which are the best ways to mitigate conflict inside the organizations, in order to diminish the degree of entropy / uncertainty in the interaction between departments and hierarchies, and to transmit to the outside world an image of cohesion and ability to fulfil the specified mission.

Whether we consider a firm or any other type of organization, communication is a vital instrument to attain goals. In this respect, both the internal and the external dimensions are important. Under the internal point of view, organizational communication must be an instrument available to the organization in order to involve and motivate workers and other people that collaborate in the project that the firm or the organization develops. The participation of all, in the sense of understanding that they function as pieces of a machine with a well defined role tends to be a factor of motivation and satisfaction, allowing to increase efficiency and productivity.

The performance of the individuals inside an organization depends on the perception and understanding of the organizational culture and environment. Only an efficient process of internal communication can achieve such understanding. The organization should try to transmit to their members the intended organizational culture, i.e., the set of meanings and values about the organization that they all ought to know and share.

The organization should also attempt to create, through a certain control over the internal communication, a favourable climate or environment. The environment results from the interaction among the members of the organization, but the organization should possess the means to direct the climate in a direction considered as convenient. If the members of an organization, being this a firm, a school, a public organism or a football club, incorporate their culture and are oriented to the development of a climate that is adequate for the prosperity of the institution, then the internal communication is successful and becomes a key element of the develop activity.

On the other hand, the organization must be capable of presenting itself to the society in a harmonious way and speaking at a single voice. Once again, the capacity to communicate is fundamental. The organization should concentrate its communication efforts with the outside world on an agent with capacity and skills to face different external stimuli and requirements. A good external communication means transmitting messages that are coherent but that can be adapted to different audiences – from the effective and potential investors to the clients or consumers associated to the activity of the organization.

Another context of communication is the one that corresponds to the interaction between a speaker and its public or audience. The communication in this context receives the designation of mass communication.

Differently from the interpersonal communication, mass communication does not involve an interactive relation between a sender and a receiver, in which permanent feedback exists. In mass communication, interaction is not so evident and the roles of the players will be from the start better defined. Besides this, mass communication is characterized by using, generally, a means or a channel that involves some kind of technological instrument, as the television, the radio, a newspaper or a book.

We should be careful not to confuse the context with the device used to convey the message. Mass communication can succeed without resorting to any technological means, solely through the direct contact between a speaker and its audience, as when a politician gives a speech or an artist performs live.

It is not the presence of absence of a given technology that characterizes and defines the mass communication. It will be the set of distinctive characteristics of its players and the way the process undergoes. In the interpersonal communication we have an individualized process from both parts (the one that conveys the message and the one that receives it); in mass communication not only the audience has a large dimension, involving too many individuals to be possible a personal interaction, but also the sender tends to organize itself as a highly complex entity that requires a rigorous and well thought planning regarding the form in which the message is passed on to the audience.

In mass communication, the necessity of a detailed planning is attached to the increased uncertainty that the communication in this context involves. On one hand, the interaction and the feedback are small; on the other hand, the audience carries for the sender a significant degree of anonymity that turns harder the transmission of messages. Because the audience to which the communication is directed to is wide, then it will necessarily also be heterogeneous what will be an additional obstacle that the mass communicator faces; probably, the message produces the desired effect onto a share of the members of the audience, but others will certainly receive it with indifference.

The mass communication means are today an important vehicle to disseminate information and as an instrument of socialization. Therefore, we should expect a homogenization or a convergence of ways of being and thinking, that becomes even more relevant if we take into account that the mass media tend to transmit messages that are highly stylized, stereotyped and repetitive. Thus, even without involving a significant interaction, or maybe exactly because of this, mass communication is a fundamental element to the development of a social and cultural identity.

Mass communication finds its reason to exist in the means that it can explore. These, as referred, are means capable of reaching large audiences but they are also means only capable of producing a repetitive and undifferentiated message for a heterogeneous public that possesses few possibilities of feedback concerning the received message. The effectiveness of a given message, for instance a commercial ad, implies a relevant effort of the communication agent in order to understand in an indirect way how the message is reaching the intended publics. The development of new technologies has somehow changed this reality.

The development of the internet has allowed for new communication forms that until recently were not seen as possible to implement. The new mean or new technology of communication preserves some of the potential of mass communication, namely the possibility of sharing messages with wide audiences, but simultaneously it can surpass some of the obstacles that the one-directional communication of means as the television or the radio impose. Communication through new technologies allows in a larger extent the interaction and the feedback, allows also to know better the different publics and to send to these, at a low cost, personal messages giving an increased power to the receiver to shape at her will the process of communication.

The new information technologies are able to re-unit and conciliate the mass communication and the interpersonal communication. The transmission of messages that are rigorously planned for target audiences can now be fulfilled simultaneously with a process of interaction in which the players alternate in their positions as senders and receivers. With the new means, the exchange of information is possible in the presence of a significant quantity of players. Each agent has now, in a way that was never possible in the past, the power to individually and by its own initiative to start large scale communication relations, independently of location and distance.

The internet came to initiate a new communication era. This is the era of un-massifying, in which means of communication that allow to reach large audiences are also means through which interactivity at the personal level is possible. This interactivity occurs in a flexible way, at the moments of time that are chosen by the parties and relatively to which considerations of spatial order become increasingly irrelevant.

1.5. FINAL NOTES

With this first chapter, we have intended to clarify that communication is a complex process that is intrinsic to social interaction. As a social being, the human being needs to interact and for this reason she has developed a set of languages and symbols that allow transmitting and share meanings.

We have argued that communication is a process. This means that the involved agents always have a relevant role. The notion that a part of the agents assumes the active position of encoding and sending a message while the other part is limited to receive and interpret passively the message, does not make sense. Most of the times the separation between a sender and a receiver will be equivocal and the interpretation of the meaning of a received message is far from being a passive act: the interpretative capacity of the one who receives some content is one of the most important elements of any communication process.

By looking at the structure of the communication process, we find many variables involved and we understand that the nature of the communication is modified by a significant variety of factors, from the context to the technology used to make the message follow its way. The diversity of the messages that are transmitted is an additional factor implying the existence of many different types of communication processes. For instance, certain messages appeal more to emotions, others involve simply the rational processing of information.

We have intended, throughout the previous sections, to transmit the idea that the communication is a complex process, since it involves simultaneously a large group of entities, but it is also a process that can be interpreted in its general traits, attributing a given order to its components. We have also concluded that the communication is dynamic, evolves in time, what constitutes an additional element of complexity that has to be accounted for.

Even the communication theory itself diverges in the interpretation it makes of its own object of study. While some authors, as Craig (1993), assert that it is necessary for the communication theory to resort to other human and social sciences to better define its placement and its frontiers, others, as Berger (1992), point to the specificity of the symbolic interaction process as the distinctive characteristic of this theoretic field, that emancipates it relatively to the other social and human sciences.

In the following chapters, we will be modelling some of the general traits of the communication process, with the intention of capturing the idea of dynamic interaction and also of revealing the complexity that the process carries. It is evident that the modelling process requires some compromises; it is impossible, through a single model, to capture the whole of the reality. On the contrary, we should understand that each analytical structure to present respects solely to some specific points of the complex system that has been described. However, the dynamic perspective will be always present; the models to develop will take variables that obey to some specified rules of intertemporal motion.

Chapter 2

A MODEL OF COMMUNICATION AND CHOICES

Communication is a complex process. This was the idea that one has tried to emphasize with the initial chapter. The variables involved in the communication process are of multiple nature and are associated with such different issues as the engineering of the processing and sending of messages or as the set of human emotions that determine attitudes and behaviors.

The richness of the process makes it hard to undertake an analysis that is simultaneously rigorous and comprehensive. To formalize a model that searches for the characterization of the key relations that communication carries, some simplifying assumptions have to be taken. The model that is developed in this chapter is a relatively simple model and, thus, incapable of providing explanations for a significant part of the doubts that were raised in the previous chapter. Nevertheless, it will be a first paradigm that illustrates and clarifies a few fundamental points of the communication process.

Particularly, in the model that is developed in this chapter we will not dissect the communication process (we will not discuss the contents of the messages and their process of encoding and decoding). Instead, we will assume from the start the existence of a communication mechanism, which produces for a given agent a set of results or expected rewards and, then, over the communication results the agent produces choices. The fundamental characteristics of the model are summarized in the following ideas.

(i) It is a dynamic model. This means that a set of differential equations will describe the process by which the assumed variables evolve through consecutive time moments. We will be interested in understanding how the differential equations translate a dynamic behavior or a behavior of temporal evolution. Our main concern is not with the mathematical tools that are used but with how they can serve to better understand the communication process. A generic analysis of dynamic models can be found, among others, in Hale and Koçak (1991), Lorenz (1993), Barro and Sala-i-Martin (1995) and Gomes (2009).

The consideration of a dynamic model is relevant in the sense that we have presented communication as a dynamic process that obeys to specific rules but that above all reflects a reality in constant evolution over time.

(ii) The model will reveal the fundamental conflict between learning and entropy. The model to develop is based, on one hand, on the generic analysis of dynamic systems in a context of adaptive learning that is studied by Sato, Akiyama and Farmer (2002),

Sato and Crutchfield (2003) and Sato, Akiyama and Crutchfield (2004), and, on the other hand, on the influent model of discrete choice that McFadden (1973), Manski and McFadden (1981) and Anderson, de Palma and Thisse (1993) have developed and that has served multiple applications, for example the work by Brock and Hommes (1997, 1998, 2002) relating the explanation of the intertemporal behavior of relevant financial and economic variables.

In what concerns learning, the model assumes an agent involved in a communication process, which in each moment of time updates her beliefs and in consequence also her actions. The agent will receive messages, but these do not produce an immediate and absolute effect: the new received information will add to the already accumulated knowledge, that was gathered as the result of previous communication and, therefore, the agent will progressively learn and change the underlying behavior through the learning that the communication stimulates.

On the other hand, entropy will arise through a loss of memory parameter, which will translate the idea that the actions followed by agents will hardly be the result of a completely noise free decision. There is noise in the sense that the individual that receives the messages and reflects them in her behavior might, in this case, have low sensitivity to past results, what will misguide the choice.

(iii) It is a model essentially focused in the receiver. As remarked in the previous chapter, the communication process involves players, giving no exclusive role to the agents in terms of the sending and receiving functions. Nevertheless, and although the richness of interpretation that the model will allow, the analysis will be simpler if we think about an individual that receives messages, processes them and adds them to her knowledge concerning a given subject, influencing in this way the respective behavior.

(iv) It is not a mechanicist model. We do not assume a straightforward process through which an agent receives a message, assimilates it and modifies the behavior following the corresponding interpretation. More specifically, the human dimension will be present in the process that we intend to describe and therefore it is not a completely mechanicist view. When receiving a message, the agent will be able to attribute various different interpretations; some will be help the agent in adopting a behavior that furnishes evident benefits, other interpretations will be less successful. Besides the ability to choose, the model also assumes that the transmitted messages are not correlated; each new message will add to the knowledge previously accumulated by the agent without changing the nature of such stock of knowledge.

Learning, capacity of choice, memory and the possibility of diverse interpretations are human characteristics, which in the present case will be incorporated in a stylized model in order to allow for a framework capable of better understanding the human interaction through communication.

The chapter is organized as follows. Section 2.1 presents the variables and the equations of motion associated to the interpretation of the communication process that is developed. The dynamics of the model is approached in section 2.2, where we discuss the existence and characterize the long-run steady-state or equilibrium result.

Section 2.3 introduces learning dynamics: the way in which we learn and interpret a message will depend on the previously gathered knowledge concerning the same subject (and, eventually, also about other subjects); therefore, it is not correct to consider that the learning capacity is constant in time, and this section will precisely formalize a rule through which the evolution of the capacity to apprehend knowledge has impact over the way the communication process evolves.

In section 2.4, the developed model is adapted to a scenario of interaction; interaction will imply that the choices made by others have influence over the benefits or rewards that each agent may withdraw from the undertaken choices. To consider social interaction in the model of choices is a way of emphasizing that communication is a process of interaction and that mutual persuasion produces two way results: the messages we send will influence the choices of others and equally our own choices.

Section 2.5 presents a set of exercises and applications.

2.1. Structural Elements of the Model

We begin by assuming an agent of the communication process that, at each time moment, will choose any action i from a set of N options: $i=1, 2, ..., N$. This choice is influenced by the symbolic interaction between this and a multiplicity of other agents.

The choice of the agent is not known but it is possible to attribute probabilities to the different options available to the individual in order for this to take the corresponding decision. Let $x_i(t)$ be the probability of the agent adopting behavior i (the probability of choosing action i), at the time moment t. Let us consider the vector $\mathbf{x}(t)=[x_1(t), x_2(t), ..., x_N(t)]$ that represents the distribution of choices. As it is obvious, the sum of all the probabilities in the distribution of the choice will correspond to the unity: $\sum_{n=1}^{N} x_n(t) = 1$.

The probability assigned to each one of the eventual options of choice is influenced by the contents of the messages the agent receives, and for this reason the distribution of choice is not unchangeable over time; on the contrary, the probabilities of choice evolve constantly as a function of an adaptation mechanism relatively to the new information that is received at each instant of time (and of the way it is received; recall from section 1 the relevance of persuasion).

The adaptation mechanism that is shaped by the communication process involves the following characteristics. First of all, each new received message is a source of information about the multiple possibilities of choice that the agent possesses. At each period of time, the agent will be able to form in a subjective way an evaluation about the benefits of the decision to make. We assume, in order to keep the model relatively simple, that this evaluation can be quantified, and thus we define $a_i(t)$ as the benefit or utility that the agent withdraws at moment t when choosing behavior i, $i=1, 2, ..., N$. This utility level translates the interpretation that the agent makes of the messages she receives systematically over time. If the communication process becomes repetitive and the received message is always the same, then $a_i(t)$ will be a constant value.

Variable $a_i(t)$ will be, in this chapter, assumed as an exogenous variable, i.e., we will not look inside the communication process; instead we will address the impact that the process has on the choices of agents. We are interested in knowing the response that the communication stimulus will produce and how the decisions are the outcome of the symbolic interaction.

The adaptation mechanism needs to consider, as well, the evaluation that the agent does of the expected benefits of adopting a given course of action. Let $Q_i(t)$ be a variable that reflects the interpretation that the agent does at moment t of the set of stimuli received in the past concerning a given alternative i, $i=1, 2, ..., N$. We consider that $\mathbf{Q}(t)=[Q_1(t), Q_2(t), ..., Q_N(t)]$ corresponds to the vector of memory variables; this includes at each moment t, the evaluation that is made by the considered agent about each one of the available options, taking into account not the last received message but the set of all past messages generated by the communication process relating to the decision that has to be taken.

The memory variables are updated at each moment according to the following rule:

$$\dot{Q}_i(t) = a_i(t) - \alpha.Q_i(t), \quad i = 1,...,N, \quad Q_i(0) = 0 \tag{2.1}$$

Equation (2.1) is a differential equation that characterizes the motion in time of variable $Q_i(t)$. Note that $\dot{Q}_i(t) \equiv dQ_i(t)/dt$, i.e., the term in the left hand side of Equation (2.1) corresponds to the derivative of the variable relatively to time, and consequently reflects the temporal evolution of the variable intending to express the value that at each moment the agent attributes to option i. The rule according to which variables $Q_i(t)$ evolve in time is expressed in the right hand side of the equation; obviously, the value attributed to each option increases [in other words, the variation of $Q_i(t)$ is positive] with the increase in the utility that is perceived through communication.

Besides the process through which the agent adds value to each one of the available options, accumulating this value to all past expected results, a memory component needs to be considered as well. We assume a memory parameter, $0<\alpha<1$, which corresponds to the rate of loss of relevance attributed to past results. Therefore, at every time moment each $Q_i(t)$ increases its value because new information about each option i becomes available through the communication process, but each $Q_i(t)$ will decrease as the result of a memory effect that turns past communication and the influence it exerts to fall with time. Notice that we also define an initial moment for the process, $t=0$. As it is evident, at the initial moment no accumulated result is available because the communication process is starting at this specific date; in (2.1) the initial value of the variable that quantifies the value attributed to each alternative of choice is logically equal to zero.

A third central element of the adaptation mechanism corresponds to the rule that updates the probabilities of choice. In the presence of variables $Q_i(t)$, which are the result of attributing meanings derived from the communication interaction, the agent will have to transform such variables into probabilities of choice, and she will make it following the model of discrete choice developed by McFadden (1973). According to this model, the correspondence between $x_i(t)$ and $Q_i(t)$ is given by the following rule,

$$x_i(t) = \frac{e^{\beta.Q_i(t)}}{\sum_{n=1}^{N} e^{\beta.Q_n(t)}}, \quad i = 1,2,...,N \tag{2.2}$$

Expression (2.2) reveals which are the elements that determine the evolution through time of the agent's probabilities of choice. Variable $Q_i(t)$ will obviously have a positive effect over the probability of choosing option i. More specifically, the higher is the value of $Q_i(t)$ relatively to the value that the communication process attributes to the set of other possibilities of choice [relatively to the value of other variables $Q_n(t)$], the more likely will be the choice of option i by the assumed agent.

Parameter β will be a positive constant that controls the learning or adaptation rate. This parameter receives the designation of intensity of choice. The value of the parameter will indicate how the evaluation of options that communication allows for contributes to modify the distribution of choices. If the value of β is low, i.e., near zero, then it is not likely a change in the distribution of choices as the result of a modification in the value of the variables $Q_i(t)$. In the extreme case $\beta=0$, the expected utility of past options will have no impact over the choice probabilities and therefore every action will have the same attached probability, $x_i(t)=1/N$. Thus, under $\beta=0$ the choice is completely random, because independently of the messages that are being transmitted and that allow to change the relative weight of each option, the additional information is not used by the agent in order to make any change on the interpretation of the problem that she faces and on the attitudes that are taken.

A high value of the intensity of choice signifies that the behavior of the agent is sensitive to the change on the expected results and therefore the symbolic interaction has relevant influence over the possibilities of choice. In the limit, when β tends to infinity, there will be no mechanism of adaptation: the option that presents a larger accumulated value in what concerns past results will be chosen with probability equal to 1.

The mechanism that we have described may be synthesized into a single equation, which will characterize the variation rate of each probability $x_i(t)$ over time. To present the intended differential equation we start by differentiating Equation (2.2) with respect to time, to get

$$\frac{\dot{x}_i(t)}{x_i(t)} = \beta.\left[\dot{Q}_i(t) - \sum_{n=1}^{N}\dot{Q}_n(t).x_n(t)\right]$$

Replacing in this result the differential equations respecting to $Q_i(t)$, $i=1, 2, ..., N$, in (2.1), one observes that:

$$\frac{\dot{x}_i(t)}{x_i(t)} = \beta.\left[a_i(t) - \sum_{n=1}^{N}a_n(t).x_n(t)\right] - \alpha.\left[\beta.Q_i(t) - \beta.\sum_{n=1}^{N}Q_n(t).x_n(t)\right]$$

Noticing that $\beta.Q_i(t) = \ln x_i(t) + \ln\sum_{n=1}^{N}e^{\beta.Q_n(t)}$ and

$\beta.\sum_{n=1}^{N}Q_n(t).x_n(t) = \sum_{n=1}^{N}\left[\ln x_i(t) + \ln\sum_{n=1}^{N}e^{\beta.Q_n(t)}\right].x_n(t)$, with the right-hand side of this

last expression equal to $\sum_{n=1}^{N}x_n(t).\ln x_n(t) + \ln\sum_{n=1}^{N}e^{\beta.Q_n(t)}$, we arrive to the differential

equation reflecting the time evolution of each probability of choice,

$$\frac{\dot{x}_i(t)}{x_i(t)} = \beta \left[a_i(t) - \sum_{n=1}^{N} a_n(t).x_n(t) \right] - \alpha \left[\ln x_i(t) - \sum_{n=1}^{N} x_n(t).\ln x_n(t) \right] \qquad (2.3)$$

$$i = 1, 2, ..., N$$

In Equation (2.3), the probability of choice of each one of the options i=1, 2, ..., N, is modified exclusively as the result of the value of the probability itself and of the evolution of the exogenous variables $a_i(t)$, which attribute value to the different choices as the result of the communication interaction. Besides this, parameters α and β play fundamental roles.

Equation (2.3) evidences two terms (on the right-hand side); each one of these terms reflects an effect of the communication process over the evaluation of the choices of behavior. The first term corresponds to an element of dynamic adaptation. This term reveals the way through which the probability of choice is influenced by the benefits that the communication process allows to identify relatively to each alternative. In this term, parameter β arises as a parameter of velocity of adaptation: the response that the probability variable will give to the change in $a_i(t)$, i=1, 2, ..., N, will depend on the value of the intensity of choice. The second term in (2.3) describes the process of memory loss, with α representing the velocity at which the loss of memory occurs. Sato, Akiyama and Crutchfield (2004) describe the term $-\ln x_i(t)$ as a variable of self-information or degree of surprise when action i is selected, while $\sum_{n=1}^{N} x_n(t).\ln x_n(t)$ can be interpreted as a measure of average self-information, also designated by Shannon entropy [Cover and Thomas (1991), van Siclen (1997), Lachman, Newman and Moore (1999), Feldman and Crutchfield (2002) and Chen (2004), are some examples of the use of the notion of entropy in the analysis of subjects related with concepts of communication and memory].

The concept of entropy measures the impact of parameter α in the process of choice. A process suffers from entropy if the past results are easily forgotten in the evaluation of the various choice options. Entropy measures the degree of choice capacity among different alternatives: a high degree of entropy is synonymous of incapacity to correctly evaluate the received messages and to use them in a conscious way to select the best option.

Based in the previous reasoning, an increase on the value of the probability $x_i(t)$ is the result of one of two events,

1) 1) the expected result of action i is higher than the expected average result of all the other choice options $\left[a_i(t) > \sum_{n=1}^{N} a_n(t).x_n(t) \right]$;

2) 2) there is a lower level of entropy associated with action i then the average value of entropy regarding the set of all the possible actions $\left[\ln x_i(t) < \sum_{n=1}^{N} x_n(t).\ln x_n(t) \right]$.

With the previous arguments, we have characterized a possible model of communication. It is not a structure aimed at an exhaustive explanation of the communication process, since it neglects a significant part of the process: the one that is found previously to the attribution of meanings. In reality, the proposed mechanism begins with attributing interpretations or meanings, which are translated on the results $a_i(t)$. Given the imposition of these results, the agent will then undertake her choices.

Nevertheless, it is a model of communication in the sense that the realization of choices is influenced by the process of symbolic interaction that communication establishes. In this process, the agent learns and this learning determines choices. In the process the agent also forgets, and the loss of memory also influences the choices and therefore it is a decisive factor in influencing attitudes and behaviors.

In a simple and synthetic way, we can characterize this model as a structure of dynamic analysis that ignores relevant issues and important variables of communication to focus the attention in a specific point that is vital to the understanding of the process: the balance between the recognition of results and learning (elements that tend to concentrate choices on the actions that display better expected outcomes) and entropy / loss of memory (that contributes to a harder choice between available options).

In the following sections, the dynamics of the model is addressed. In a first moment, we determine the long-run result and we search for the dynamic behavior underlying the model that is condensed into Equation (2.3). Afterwards, we introduce additional features into the model; specifically, we will analyze how learning eventually modifies the structure of the problem and we will also discuss interaction through communication.

2.2. DYNAMICS AND STEADY STATE

To study the dynamic behavior of the model, we define variable $\phi(t) \equiv \dfrac{x_i(t)}{x_j(t)}$, for any actions i and j in the considered domain. This variable measures the probability of choice of action i relatively to the probability of choice of any other action, j. This probability ratio can be used to build a new equation of motion; precisely the equation that establishes the law of motion for the new variable. Recognizing that $\dfrac{\dot{\phi}(t)}{\phi(t)} = \dfrac{\dot{x}_i(t)}{x_i(t)} - \dfrac{\dot{x}_j(t)}{x_j(t)}$, then, considering Equation (2.3) for actions i and j we find, through the corresponding subtraction,

$$\frac{\dot{\phi}(t)}{\phi(t)} = \beta.[a_i(t) - a_j(t)] - \alpha.\ln \phi(t), \quad i, j = 1, 2, ..., N \tag{2.4}$$

Equation (2.4) is a differential equation with a unique endogenous variable, and for this reason its dynamic behavior is relatively easy to characterize (to simplify the analysis, we assume for now that a_i and a_j are constants).

The first important result that (2.4) reveals is the existence of a long run equilibrium point, which is found by establishing condition $\dot{\phi}(t) = 0$. In this circumstance, we find

$$\overline{\phi} = e^{\frac{\beta}{\alpha}.(a_i - a_j)} \tag{2.5}$$

According to (2.5), if we assume that there is a long-run steady state in which the probabilities of choice reach a fixed value that will be changed only if some perturbation in the parameters or in the exogenous variables of the model occurs, it is possible to identify what determines the relative value between probabilities of choice in the long-term.

Through the identification of the determinants of choice we will understand which are the factors in the communication process interfering with the behavior of agents. As it is evident, the long-run value of the ratio $\phi(t)$ is larger than one when the expected reward associated to action i is larger than the expected reward associated to action j. If, on the contrary, $a_i < a_j$, then the equilibrium value of the ratio will be lower than one, meaning that the probability assigned to the choice of action i will be inferior to the probability of choice of action j.

The results relating parameters α and β are also intuitive results. The higher the value of the parameter of memory loss, the smaller will be the distance from $\overline{\phi}$ relatively to the unity, what reflects a small distance between the values of the probabilities of choice. In what concerns the intensity of choice, the larger the value of β the more $\overline{\phi}$ will depart from the unity, what signifies that a strong probability of choice will be assigned to one of the options regardless of alternative options. With a large value of β, the probabilities ratio will be close to zero for $a_i < a_j$, and it will be significantly above one in the case in which the opposite condition holds.

The dynamics associated with Equation (2.4) can be analyzed through the graphical representation of the associated phase diagram. The phase diagram relates the value of the variable with the corresponding variation; in this way, one will be able to characterize the dynamic behavior of the variable: the corresponding value grows with positive variations, decreasing otherwise. The phase diagram of figure 2.1, respecting to the dynamics of Equation (2.4), reveals that the equilibrium point (2.5) is stable, i.e., independently of the location of the initial point $\phi(0)$, the system tends to the equilibrium point.

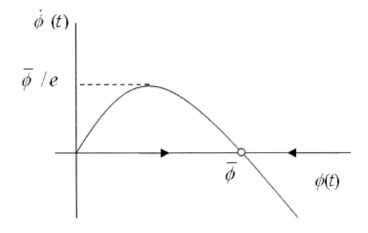

Figure 2.1. Phase diagram relating the dynamics of the probabilities of choice ratio.

Figure 2.1 synthesizes the dynamics of the model. For $\dfrac{x_i(0)}{\overline{x}_i} < \dfrac{x_j(0)}{\overline{x}_j}$, i.e., when the distance between the initial value of the probability and the corresponding equilibrium value is lower for action i than for action j, then the variation of the ratio $\phi(t)$ is positive and the system converges to the steady state. If $\dfrac{x_i(0)}{\overline{x}_i} > \dfrac{x_j(0)}{\overline{x}_j}$, then $x_i(t)$ decreases relatively to $x_j(t)$ as the system converges to the steady state.

The shape of the function in figure 2.1 is dependent on the values of the parameters in (2.4). Noticing that the equilibrium value of the ratio between probabilities is dependent on the relation between rewards a_i and a_j we understand that the extent in which the variation of the value of the ratio between probabilities is positive is as much higher as the higher is the value of a_i relatively to a_j. Also the ratio between β and α has implications over the extension of the areas in the graphic where the variation of the value of the ratio is positive and negative.

Figure 2.1 allows concluding that the model is stable: the probabilities of choice converge to a long-run result consisting of an intermediate value, i.e., there will be no tendency for a divergence process that would imply asymptotically choosing one of the options with probability 1. The distribution of choices is maintained constant in the long-run, unless some exogenous perturbation over parameters succeeds.

The only exception to the result in figure 2.1 relates to the absence of entropy. For $\alpha=0$ there is no long-run equilibrium and the dynamic evolution of $\phi(t)$ follows the pattern presented in figure 2.2. In this case, the variation of $\phi(t)$ will be always positive (if $a_i>a_j$), what indicates that the value of the variable tends to infinity, or always negative (if $a_i<a_j$), case in which the ratio of probabilities tends to zero. Therefore, in the absence of memory loss, in the long-run the agent will reveal certainty relatively to the choice to undertake, since one of the possibilities of choice will concentrate the whole probability. Figure 2.2 presents the first case, $a_i>a_j$.

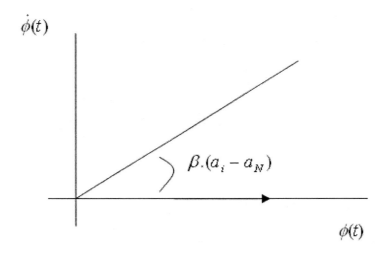

Figure 2.2. Phase diagram concerning the dynamics of variable $\phi(t)$ under $\alpha=0$.

The extreme case of figure 2.2 indicates the relevance of a communication process with low levels of information loss, noise or entropy. In this circumstance the process of communication will be as much efficient as the lower is the value of α, since in this case the choice will be made without any degree of uncertainty; the higher is the value of this parameter the more the value of the ratio of probabilities approaches 1, what means the impossibility of making a choice under certainty. Thus, the loss of memory is an element leading to an inefficient result that can be fought through a learning process capable of allowing for the increase in the intensity of choice.

In our model of communication and choice, the previous reasoning allows to clarify ideas about what is a process of efficient communication: this will be the process where high levels of memory and learning are put together to push the equilibrium point in the graphic of figure 2.1 into the direction of one of its extremes (zero or infinity); the closer the equilibrium value is to zero or to infinity more certainty will exist relatively to the choice to be undertaken and, therefore, a communication process where the doubts of the agents facing multiple choices are eliminated is then fulfilled.

As it is evident, and according with the discussion in section 2.1, the efficiency in communication is something much more complex than the simple elimination of doubts and uncertainties relating the choice that needs to be made. Since it is a complex and intertemporal process, the communication process can contain other objectives besides the simple auxiliary role regarding decision making. Nevertheless, in the developed model, communication arises mainly as a way to help in the decision process. Communication is useful in the sense that it turns decisions easier, by leading the probabilities of choice towards extreme points.

In order to turn the previous analysis clearer we can consider a particular case with only two possibilities of choice ($N=2$). Given this scenario, the distribution of choices is composed solely by two elements, $x_1(t)$ and $x_2(t)=1-x_1(t)$.

Equation (2.3) can be rewritten, for only two possibilities of choice, including a unique endogenous variable, $x_1(t)$. Specifically, we will have the following dynamic equation characterizing the impact of communication over probabilities of choice,

$$\frac{\dot{x}_1(t)}{x_1(t)} = \{\beta.(a_1 - a_2) - \alpha.[\ln x_1(t) - \ln(1 - x_1(t))]\}.[1 - x_1(t)] \tag{2.6}$$

In (2.6), a_1 and a_2 represent the expected benefits of each one of the eventual choices. In possession of Equation (2.6) we can present an equilibrium result, which reveals the existence of a long-run constant probability of action 1 being chosen instead of option 2. This result is given by (2.7).

$$\overline{x}_1 = \frac{e^{\frac{\beta}{\alpha}.(a_1 - a_2)}}{1 + e^{\frac{\beta}{\alpha}.(a_1 - a_2)}} \tag{2.7}$$

The most evident property of the equilibrium result (2.7) is that the long-run probability of the choice corresponding to action 1 being equal, lower or higher than 50% will depend on the relation between the values of the expected rewards, i.e.,

$$a_1 = a_2 \Rightarrow \overline{x}_1 = 1/2;$$
$$a_1 > a_2 \Rightarrow \overline{x}_1 > 1/2;$$
$$a_1 < a_2 \Rightarrow \overline{x}_1 < 1/2.$$

We also observe that the ratio between β and α produces one of two effects. An increase on the value of this ratio (which implies that learning capacities increase relatively to memory loss) will imply that the equilibrium value of the probability $x_1(t)$ will approach zero (for $a_1 < a_2$) or unity (for $a_1 > a_2$), what once again reflects the idea that more learning or more rationality combined with lower entropy makes the probabilities of choice to approach extreme values, reducing in this way the uncertainties attached to the decision process.

The equilibrium is again stable, as in the generic case. Consequently, the system produces a set of two probabilities of fixed value in the long-run and the dynamics of the model is determined by the convergence process towards such stable equilibrium. Figure 2.3 represents the phase diagram for probability $x_1(t)$. We verify, through the graphic, that between 0 and the equilibrium value, the variation in the probability is positive, implying convergence to the steady state. To the right of the equilibrium point, between this and the unity, the variation of the probability is negative, what again implies a stability situation, in this case with the initial value of the probability of choice above the steady state value, with this value decreasing until the steady state point is reached.

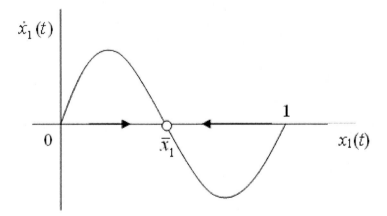

Figure 2.3. Phase diagram relating the dynamics of $x_1(t)$, for $N=2$.

Once again, the exception to the existence of an equilibrium point somewhere between the extreme values of probabilities is the case of absence of memory loss or absence of entropy. For $\alpha=0$, Equation (2.6) is reduced to $\dfrac{\dot{x}_1(t)}{x_1(t)} = \beta.(a_1 - a_2).[1 - x_1(t)]$, what in graphical terms implies the existence of a function displaying no intermediate steady-state.

The probability of choice will converge to zero or to one depending on if the expected reward of option 1 is lower or higher, respectively, than the expected reward of option 2.

As one verifies by looking at figure 2.4, the change in $x_1(t)$ will be always positive in the direction of the unity, for $a_1 > a_2$ and it will be always negative, in the direction of zero, in the case in which $a_1 < a_2$.

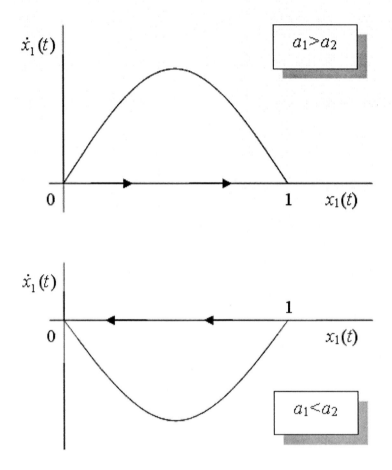

Figure 2.4. Phase diagram relating to the dynamics of $x_1(t)$, for $N=2$ and $\alpha=0$.

The analysis in this section has allowed for the formalization of some of the notions and mechanisms one has considered in the first chapter. Basically, we have found three nuclear purposes of communication regarding its contribution to the formulation of choices:

- first, communication allows to attribute value to options of choice. Only through the sharing of messages one can collect information and form beliefs through the persuasion process, and it will be in this way that individuals will be able to compare the available choices, taking decisions based on the expected value of each one of the available choices;

- second, communication is central to the minimization of entropy associated with the choice process. Efficient communication will be synonymous of transmission of messages that are perpetuated in terms of memory;
- finally, communication encloses a process of learning. Through communication, one gains a capacity to evaluate different alternatives, making the process of choice easier. In the undertaken analysis, learning was addressed by simply taking a constant parameter through which one measures the capacity of adaptation to new data produced by the communication process; in the next section, we introduce the possibility of having a dynamic learning component in the model. The way in which dynamic learning changes the choice process is, then, discussed in section 2.3.

2.3. LEARNING DYNAMICS

Being a dynamic process, communication is also a learning process. Through communication we gain conscience of the problems we face and of the way we can react in an efficient manner to the challenges that we are confronted with. Two individuals placed for the first time face to face will demonstrate relatively low propensity to change their distribution of choices, or, in other words, their intensity of choice will certainly correspond to a low value.

As the interaction between them is developed, they will better understand the scenario where they are playing, they will understand and be able to predict the behavior and the reactions of the other party and, in synthesis, they will learn with the interaction process in order to better evaluate the expected outcomes; thus, the intensities of choice become more flexible, i.e., the probabilities of choice are changed in a more immediate way, when the expected results justify such change, as the knowledge concerning the assumed process becomes more complete.

In the model of communication and choices it will be parameter β, the intensity of choice, that will translate the capacity of the agent in responding to the change in expected results. Understanding β as a learning parameter, it will make sense to assume that this is not a constant value throughout the considered temporal horizon in which the communication process occurs. By assuming that the intensity of choice evolves in time according to some differential equation rule we can get a more complete picture of the choices scenario.

Two simple and logical assumptions will be enough to represent a dynamic equation respecting the time evolution of the learning variable:

a) Learning is cumulative. More accumulated knowledge implies a faster learning;

b) Learning is subject to decreasing marginal returns. The additional increase in learning will be as much lower as the more knowledge as been previously accumulated. This means essentially that there is a limit to the learning process. When the interaction between two or more sides has already produced a high degree of mutual knowledge, it is possible that a deeper relation adds some new knowledge, but such increase tends to be progressively smaller.

Defining $\beta(t)$ as the learning variable, the differential equation respecting to the time evolution of this variable will be written as:

$$\dot{\beta}(t) = B.\beta(t)^b - \delta.\beta(t), \quad \beta(0) = 0 \qquad (2.8)$$

In (2.8), $b \in (0,1)$ is the parameter revealing the intensity of the decreasing returns; the closer the value of b is to one the smaller will be the intensity of the decreasing returns and therefore the more the intensity of choice contributes for a larger amount of knowledge generated by learning. Parameter $\delta > 0$ will be the rate of obsolescence of knowledge, i.e., we assume that knowledge is possible to be accumulated in time, however there is also a process of unlearning: the agents also lose through time capacity to learn as they forget some peculiarities of the interaction process. Parameter B is a positive constant.

The intensity of choice is now a variable that depends on time. This means that the model presented in section 2.1 will lead to a modified version of the dynamic equation relating the probabilities of choice, (2.3). To arrive to the new equation of motion for $x_i(t)$, we proceed as before, starting by differentiating with respect to time an expression similar to (2.2), which we distinguish from this by the fact that the intensity of choice is no longer constant. From the differentiation procedure we obtain

$$\frac{\dot{x}_i(t)}{x_i(t)} = \beta.\left[\dot{Q}_i(t) - \sum_{n=1}^{N} \dot{Q}_n(t).x_n(t) \right] + \dot{\beta}(t).\left[Q_i(t) - \sum_{n=1}^{N} Q_n(t).x_n(t) \right]$$

Replacing (2.1) in this expression, we find the new equation giving the time motion of the choice probabilities:

$$\frac{\dot{x}_i(t)}{x_i(t)} = \beta.\left[a_i(t) - \sum_{n=1}^{N} a_n(t).x_n(t) \right] +$$

$$+ \left[\frac{\dot{\beta}(t)}{\beta(t)} - \alpha \right]\left[\ln x_i(t) - \sum_{n=1}^{N} x_n(t).\ln x_n(t) \right], \quad i = 1,2,...,N \qquad (2.9)$$

Comparing (2.9) with (2.3) one concludes that by turning endogenous the time motion of the intensity of choice we are basically introducing a term concerning the growth of the intensity of choice into the fundamental dynamic equation of the model. Therefore, we arrive to a relevant conclusion:

- the process by which the agent learns throughout the communicational interaction is an element allowing to reduce uncertainty or entropy. As it is evident, learning helps in the decision making process, turning this more efficient since it can lower the ambiguity or entropy associated to the choice. This result is expressed in Equation (2.9). The equation reveals that the higher is the growth rate of learning, the smaller will be the impact of the loss of memory relatively to past results over the entropy component of the choice.

Given that learning is subject to decreasing returns, in the long-run the intensity of choice will no longer have space to grow, and therefore the entropy term remains relevant in the long-term.

As in the case where no dynamics were associated to the intensity of choice, the model can be analyzed considering the ratio $\phi(t) \equiv \dfrac{x_i(t)}{x_j(t)}$. For this, the following dynamic relation holds,

$$\frac{\dot{\phi}(t)}{\phi(t)} = \beta.\left[a_i(t) - a_j(t)\right] + \left[\frac{\dot{\beta}(t)}{\beta(t)} - \alpha\right].\ln\phi(t), \quad i, j = 1, 2, ..., N \qquad (2.10)$$

In opposition to the original model, the learning model allows for two endogenous variables: the ratio between probabilities and the intensity of choice. The dynamics of the model has to be studied for the system of Equations (2.8)-(2.10). The dynamic analysis of planar equations (i.e., systems of two differential equations) involves a larger complexity than the study undertaken previously for a single equation. We will not develop in detail mathematical peculiarities regarding the analysis of the system; we just circumscribe the analysis to the fundamental issues that allow understanding the intertemporal relation between variables.

We start by characterizing the steady-state. In the long-run, the intensity of choice will be a constant value, what is a direct consequence of the assumption of decreasing marginal returns. The intensity of choice will be as much higher, in the long-run, as the larger is the value of parameters B and b, and the lower is the rate of knowledge obsolescence, δ. Specifically, $\dot{\beta}(t) = 0 \Rightarrow \overline{\beta} = \left(B\middle/\delta\right)^{1/(1-b)}$. Being the equilibrium value of the intensity of choice a constant value, the long-run equilibrium of the probabilities ratio will not depart from the result in (2.5); the only difference is that now it is possible to characterize the equilibrium value of the intensity of choice. Again, the intensity of choice allows the probabilities to approach extreme values, while the parameter of memory loss is a factor of approximation of the probability values. The equilibrium ratio of $\phi(t)$ will be larger or inferior to one according with the value of the expected rewards or outcomes of the choice, a_i and a_j.

The introduction of a new dimension in the model does not allow for the possibility of a global dynamic analysis as the one pursued in section 2.2. To understand the joint behavior of the endogenous variables $\beta(t)$ and $\phi(t)$ we will have to concentrate in a local analysis, in the vicinity of the steady-state. This analysis implies the need to compute a Jacobian matrix, which includes as elements the derivatives of each equation in order to each endogenous variable, with these derivatives evaluated in the steady-state.

The matrix one wants to compute is,

$$J = \begin{bmatrix} \dfrac{\partial \dot{\beta}(t)}{\partial \beta(t)}\bigg|_{(\bar{\beta},\bar{\phi})} & \dfrac{\partial \dot{\beta}(t)}{\partial \phi(t)}\bigg|_{(\bar{\beta},\bar{\phi})} \\[2ex] \dfrac{\partial \dot{\phi}(t)}{\partial \beta(t)}\bigg|_{(\bar{\beta},\bar{\phi})} & \dfrac{\partial \dot{\phi}(t)}{\partial \phi(t)}\bigg|_{(\bar{\beta},\bar{\phi})} \end{bmatrix}$$

The system linearized in the vicinity of the steady-state will possess the following shape,

$$\begin{bmatrix} \dot{\beta}(t) \\ \dot{\phi}(t) \end{bmatrix} = J.\begin{bmatrix} \beta(t) - \bar{\beta} \\ \phi(t) - \bar{\phi} \end{bmatrix}$$

The computation of matrix J leads to the following result,

$$J = \begin{bmatrix} -(1-b).\delta & 0 \\ \left(1 - \dfrac{1-b}{\alpha}\right).(a_i - a_j).\bar{\phi} & -\alpha \end{bmatrix} \qquad (2.11)$$

It is based on the information one obtains from J in (2.11) that it becomes possible to proceed with the dynamic analysis of the relation between learning and the distribution of probabilities. The dynamic analysis can be undertaken in two ways: graphically, by building a different kind of phase diagram relatively to the one in previous sections, or analytically through the computation of the eigenvalues associated to matrix J.

In a first phase, we proceed with the graphical analysis. To draw the phase diagram we have to start by representing two reference lines, which we will call isoclines. These correspond to the straight lines given by

$$\dot{\beta}(t) = 0 \Rightarrow \beta(t) = \bar{\beta};$$

$$\dot{\phi}(t) = 0 \Rightarrow \phi(t) = \bar{\phi} - j.\frac{\bar{\beta}}{\alpha} + \frac{j}{\alpha}.\beta(t), \quad j = \left(1 - \frac{1-b}{\alpha}\right).(a_i - a_j).\bar{\phi}.$$

In the referential $[\beta(t),\phi(t)]$, the first of the isoclines is a vertical line while the second isocline can have a positive or a negative slope, according to the sign of the combination of parameters j. In this referential, we can also represent directional arrows that indicate the direction of the flow of the variables over time. For the first isocline, we notice that

$$\dfrac{\partial \dot{\beta}(t)}{\partial \beta(t)}\bigg|_{(\bar{\beta},\bar{\phi})} < 0,$$ meaning that the value of the variable $\beta(t)$ will decrease to the right of the

corresponding isocline, increasing to its left (this result is presented in figures 2.5 and 2.6 through the lines in a horizontal position; these arrows are represented in the horizontal in order to follow the representation of the variable in the corresponding axis).

For the second isocline, we notice that $\dfrac{\partial \dot{\phi}(t)}{\partial \beta(t)}\bigg|_{(\bar{\beta},\bar{\phi})} = j$, which can be either a positive

or a negative value; if it is a positive value, situation that is considered in figure 2.5, we will have arrows pointing upwards to the right of the corresponding isocline and arrows pointing downwards to the left of $\dot{\phi}(t) = 0$. If $j<0$, as we consider in figure 2.6, then the corresponding directional arrows will have a descending direction to the right of the isocline and an ascending direction to the left of the referred isocline.

Putting together all the directional arrows we conclude, for each quadrant of the graphic, which the direction of the dynamics of the variables in the model. By looking to the figure, one concludes that independently of the initial point of the system there is a tendency for convergence to the steady-state, i.e., we find that the steady-state is a stable fixed point.

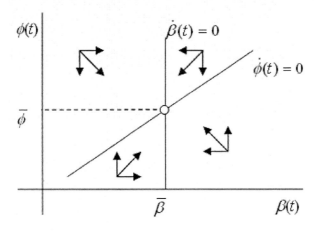

Figure 2.5. Phase diagram for the dynamic relation $\beta(t)$-$\phi(t)$ [$j>0$].

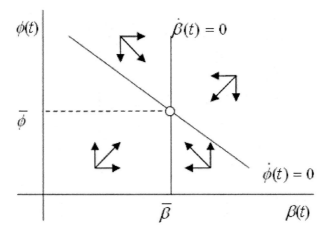

Figure 2.6. Phase diagram for the dynamic relation $\beta(t)$-$\phi(t)$ [$j<0$].

Figures 2.5 and 2.6 clearly reveal that the model is stable. Independently of the initial values $[\beta(0),\phi(0)]$, both variables converge to the corresponding steady-state, regardless from the values of parameters and of the relation between expected rewards. Thus, the introduction of learning dynamics does not change the qualitative character of the model: there will be in the long-run an array of probabilities of choice, which does not have necessarily to concentrate all the probability in a single choice and that will depend on the constant values of expected rewards, intensity of choice and loss of memory. This conclusion is possible because we have taken the assumption that the rate of learning is decreasing in such a way that it leads to a constant long-run value for the intensity of choice.

To the previous result one can also arrive, in a straightforward way, by the simple computation of the eigenvalues associated to matrix J. These are computed by solving the following characteristic equation: $\lambda^2 - Tr(J).\lambda + Det(J) = 0$, in which $Tr(J)$ and $Det(J)$ represent, respectively, the trace and the determinant of the Jacobian matrix. This equation will have two roots, λ_1 and λ_2, and there will be the signs of these two roots, which are the eigenvalues of the matrix, that will allow to characterize the dynamic behavior underlying the variables of the model.

Ignoring exceptional situations (zero eigenvalues and complex roots) three scenarios are possible: (1) the eigenvalues are both positive, what implies a situation of instability (whatever is the initial point, the dynamic process tends to make the variables to depart from the corresponding steady-state values); (2) the eigenvalues are both negative, what is a synonymous of stability (independently of the location of the starting point, there is a tendency for convergence of the endogenous variables of the model in the direction of the corresponding equilibrium); (3) a positive eigenvalue and a negative eigenvalue; in this case there exists a stable dimension and an unstable dimension. Convergence to the steady-state is only possible, in this case, if the initial point is already located over the stable trajectory, also called saddle trajectory; if such location of the initial state does not hold, then there will be divergence relatively to the equilibrium point. To this specific dynamic result is attributed the designation of saddle-path equilibrium.

The computation of the eigenvalues of matrix J in (2.11) requires the determination of the corresponding trace and determinant: $Tr(J)$=-α-(1-b).δ and $Det(J)$=α.(1-b).δ. Solving the characteristic equation, one confirms the stability of the steady-state, which we had determined through the graphical analysis:

λ_1=-α<0 and λ_2=-(1-b).δ<0.

As in the context of constant learning, the absence of entropy arises as a relevant particular case. Again, constraint α=0 leads to the absence of an intermediate equilibrium point for the probabilities of choice; for this reason, all the probability will concentrate in a unique possibility of choice. Note as well that the absence of knowledge obsolescence (δ=0) is an element producing instability; for δ=0, the accumulation of knowledge over time through learning is translated in a continuous accumulation of value by the intensity of choice that in the long-run will tend to infinity.

An infinite intensity of choice means that in each moment the agent will change instantly her perception of choices and will attribute probability 1 to the alternative that in the specific considered moment has the highest associated expected reward. Therefore, we conclude that the absence of a parameter translating loss of memory at the learning level has exactly the same effect that the absence of a parameter of memory loss concerning past rewards: this effect consists in eliminating the existence of a stable equilibrium point for the distribution of choices and, consequently, it will imply that the efficiency of the communication process will reach a maximum in the sense that the probability of choice will concentrate exclusively in the best option.

In reality, not everything we learn is retained tough time, in the same way we do not evaluate past rewards exactly as present ones. Thus, any choice process will always be enclosed in some degree of entropy; this means that communication helps in the decision making process allowing to attribute probabilities to different alternatives, however, communication will not imply the formation of absolute convictions regarding the decision process.

One of the fundamental assumptions needed in order to guarantee the result of steady-state stability is related with the type of marginal returns associated to learning. The consideration of decreasing returns was supported on the idea that as we learn more then more effort will be needed to continue learning in the sense that the space of available knowledge becomes progressively more limited. We can take the opposite direction, i.e., to consider that learning generates additional learning and that the interaction process through communication is such that at each moment it broadens the space of knowledge, making knowledge to grow progressively faster as the learning process evolves. In this reasoning it is implicit the notion of externality or spillover: The larger is the quantity of knowledge that one can resort to in order to learn more, then additional knowledge will in fact be created. This idea is expressed in the well known sentence by Isaac Newton [in a letter destined to Robert Hook, dated from February 5, 1675, and cited in Caballero and Jaffe (1993)],

"If I have seen further it is by standing on the shoulders of giants."

Under this last interpretation, parameter b in (2.8) would be a value larger than one. In the presence of increasing returns in the learning process, the intensity of choice tends to infinity as time evolves and consequently the equilibrium will no longer exist, in the same way it disappears in the absence of memory parameters. Hence, the equilibrium result according to which not only a unique option of choice is taken into account will exist if the following conditions hold:

1) The memory relatively to eventual past results is not absolute;
2) Learning is subject to obsolescence or to a process through which past events are, to a given extent, forgotten;
3) Additional learning tends to be progressively smaller, as the communication process evolves.

2.4. SOCIAL INTERACTION

Communication means to inform and to be informed, to persuade and to be persuaded. There is, clearly, an implicit process of interaction; however, the modelling structure that we have presented in previous sections does not approach this interaction. We only implicitly consider that communication allows an agent to evaluate the expected result of the choices and to learn in order to turn more efficient the decision making process.

In this section, we add to the model the idea of mutual influence. We consider two agents and the bond between them is established at the level of the expected reward. The reward expected by agent X when taking action i will depend on the reward expected by agent Y when this decides to select a given action j.

The process of social interaction is presented, in this way, under a same analytical structure as the one used until now. Other ways of facing social interaction can, obviously, be assumed; for instance Manski (1993), Glaeser, Sacerdote and Scheinkman (1996), Brock and Durlauf (2001, 2003), Durlauf (2003) and Durlauf and Cohen-Cole (2004) study the processes of social interaction having in consideration not only the way in which the characteristics and choices of others influence the individual decisions and behavior, what is basically the object of discussion in this section, but also the way the interaction provokes changes in aggregate behavior or behavior of groups.

Here, we once again emphasize the difficulty that exists in translating the processes of interaction and communication into an analytical framework. What interaction may mean involves too many variables that cannot be rigorously addressed all at once in a combined way. Therefore, even though we recognize that this is a limited notion, we define social interaction, in the present context, as translating the idea that the expected reward or utility of a given action depends directly on the choices of others.

Consider, then, the interaction between two agents. Assume that agents X and Y have available the same N choices; agent X assigns to each one of the choices a probability $x_i(t)$, $i=1, 2, ..., N$ and the agent Y will consider another vector of probabilities, that includes probabilities $y_i(t)$.

The main distinction one has to take into account relatively to the model of individual choice consists in the consideration of reward functions where it is reflected the fact that each one of the agents benefits from the choice of the other agent. The following assumption is central to the analysis:

- when agent X chooses a given option i, the agent Y will have access to an additional reward $b_i(X)$, if she chooses the exact same option;
- when agent Y chooses a given option i, the agent X will have access to an additional reward $a_i(Y)$, if she simultaneously selects the same option;
- in the case in which the choices of the two agents are different, no additional reward is assumed.

In formal terms we will have, then (once more, in order to ensure the tractability of the analysis, we consider that the rewards are exogenous and constant values),

- reward of agent X: $A_i(X) = a_i + a_i(Y).y_i(t)$;
- reward of agent Y: $B_i(Y) = b_i + b_i(X).x_i(t)$.

In these expressions, a_i and b_i correspond to the rewards of each agent, X and Y respectively, when the agents do not choose the same option (or, more rigorously, when the probability of each of the agents selecting precisely the same option i is zero).

The remaining structure of the model will be similar to the one considered in the original version. We ignore, to simplify the analysis, the growth process of the intensity of choice, assuming that this is a constant parameter value. In order to arrive to the dynamic equation that represents the time evolution of the probability of choice of a given option, for each one of the agents, we proceed as in the first assumed version, starting by differentiating with respect to time expressions that are similar to (2.2). As for (2.3), we can write the following two differential equations,

$$\frac{\dot{x}_i(t)}{x_i(t)} = \beta_X \cdot \left[A_i(X) - \sum_{n=1}^{N} A_n(X).x_n(t) \right] -$$
$$- \alpha_X \cdot \left[\ln x_i(t) - \sum_{n=1}^{N} x_n(t).\ln x_n(t) \right], \quad i = 1,2,...,N \tag{2.12}$$

$$\frac{\dot{y}_i(t)}{y_i(t)} = \beta_Y \cdot \left[B_i(Y) - \sum_{n=1}^{N} B_n(Y).y_n(t) \right] -$$
$$- \alpha_Y \cdot \left[\ln y_i(t) - \sum_{n=1}^{N} y_n(t).\ln y_n(t) \right], \quad i = 1,2,...,N \tag{2.13}$$

An important assumption that is present in this interaction structure relates to considering that agents possess different levels of intensity of choice and memory, such that in (2.12) and (2.13), we make the distinction between β_X and β_Y and between α_X and α_Y.

As one verifies by simple observation of the equations, the fundamental structure of the model of communication and choices does not differ significantly in the situations of presence or absence of interaction. The fact of the reward achieved by one of the agents being dependent on the choice made by the other does not have implications over the two fundamental components of the choice process: both the adaptation and learning process and the loss of memory and entropy component continue to characterize the assumed structure. It will be, once again, from the conflict between capacity of adaptation and entropy that it will arise a given temporal evolution and a given equilibrium result characterizing the distribution of choices. The novelty is in the fact that the efficiency in the learning and adaptation process will be dependent not only on the choice of each agent but also on the perception about the choices of others.

Once more, the dynamic analysis requires the consideration of a ratio between two probabilities of choice, i and j. We define, then, $\phi(t) \equiv \dfrac{x_i(t)}{x_j(t)}$ and $\varphi(t) \equiv \dfrac{y_i(t)}{y_j(t)}$. For these variables, we notice that

$$\frac{\dot{\phi}(t)}{\phi(t)} = \beta_X \cdot \left[A_i(X) - A_j(X) \right] - \alpha_X \cdot \ln \phi(t), \quad i, j = 1, 2,...,N \tag{2.14}$$

$$\frac{\dot{\varphi}(t)}{\varphi(t)} = \beta_Y.\left[B_i(Y) - B_j(Y)\right] - \alpha_Y.\ln\varphi(t), \quad i,j = 1,2,\dots,N \tag{2.15}$$

Equations (2.14) and (2.15) do not allow, in the form they are presented, to proceed with the dynamic analysis because the rewards will include probability variables, making the number of endogenous variables to rise above the dimension of the system. For this reason, the study of the dynamics of the model will be undertaken under one more condition, the one transforming the model in a problem of binary choice: $N=2$; also Brock and Durlauf (2001) choose to adopt a binary choice model in order to address the implications of social interaction.

For $x_j(t)=1-x_i(t)$ and $y_j(t)=1-y_i(t)$, Equations (2.14) and (2.15) are reduced to equations representing the intertemporal motion of a single probability of choice for each agent. After some computation, we obtain

$$\frac{\dot{x}_i(t)}{x_i(t).\left[1 - x_i(t)\right]} = \beta_X.\left[a_i - a_j - a_j(Y) + (a_i(Y) + a_j(Y)).y_i(t)\right] - \\ - \alpha_X.\left[\ln x_i(t) - \ln(1 - x_i(t))\right] \tag{2.16}$$

$$\frac{\dot{y}_i(t)}{y_i(t).\left[1 - y_i(t)\right]} = \beta_Y.\left[b_i - b_j - b_j(X) + (b_i(X) + b_j(X)).x_i(t)\right] - \\ - \alpha_Y.\left[\ln y_i(t) - \ln(1 - y_i(t))\right] \tag{2.17}$$

Equations (2.16) and (2.17) form a system of two differential equations with two endogenous variables, and therefore the corresponding dynamic properties can now be analyzed. The variables correspond to the probability of each agent choosing option i and not option j, given that the other agent can select action i or action j.

The computation of the solution of the system $\dot{x}_i(t) = 0; \dot{y}_i(t) = 0$ does not allow finding an explicit form for the steady-state. However, we can consider a hypothetical equilibrium result for one of the variables, let us say $y_i(t)$, to realize that the steady-state of $x_i(t)$ will correspond to a similar result relatively to the one found in the model with absence of interaction. Consider,

1) 1) In the steady-state, the agent Y does not choose option i ($\overline{y}_i = 0$); in this case,

$$\overline{x}_i = \frac{e^{\frac{\beta_X}{\alpha_x}.\left[a_i - a_j - a_j(Y)\right]}}{1 + e^{\frac{\beta_X}{\alpha_x}.\left[a_i - a_j - a_j(Y)\right]}};$$

2) 2) In the steady-state, agent Y considers choices to be indifferent ($\bar{y}_i = 1/2$); in this

circumstance, $\bar{x}_i = \dfrac{e^{\frac{\beta_x}{\alpha_x}.[a_i - a_j + 0.5.a_i(Y) - 0.5.a_j(Y)]}}{1 + e^{\frac{\beta_x}{\alpha_x}.[a_i - a_j + 0.5.a_i(Y) - 0.5.a_j(Y)]}}$.

3) 3) In the steady-state, agent Y chooses option i ($\bar{y}_i = 1$); now,

$\bar{x}_i = \dfrac{e^{\frac{\beta_x}{\alpha_x}.[a_i - a_j + a_i(Y)]}}{1 + e^{\frac{\beta_x}{\alpha_x}.[a_i - a_j + a_i(Y)]}}$.

An exercise similar to the previous one may be pursued by considering a fixed value of $x_i(t)$ in the steady-state. In the above examples we find precisely the same influences over the long-run equilibrium one has found before; the analysis of the expected rewards became more complex, however parameters α (α_X and α_Y) and β (β_X and β_Y) continue to play the same roles: lower loss of memory and higher intensity of choice are factors that allow the probability of choice to approach one of its extreme values.

Once again, the absence of any memory loss will imply that no steady-state is achievable and that the probabilities will diverge to 0 or to 1. Let us concentrate the analysis in the case in which α_X and α_Y are positive values.

In the presence of a dynamic system of dimension 2, we compute the corresponding Jacobian matrix:

$$
\mathbf{J} = \begin{bmatrix} \left.\dfrac{\partial \dot{x}_i(t)}{\partial x_i(t)}\right|_{(\bar{x}_i, \bar{y}_i)} & \left.\dfrac{\partial \dot{x}_i(t)}{\partial y_i(t)}\right|_{(\bar{x}_i, \bar{y}_i)} \\ \left.\dfrac{\partial \dot{y}_i(t)}{\partial x_i(t)}\right|_{(\bar{x}_i, \bar{y}_i)} & \left.\dfrac{\partial \dot{y}_i(t)}{\partial y_i(t)}\right|_{(\bar{x}_i, \bar{y}_i)} \end{bmatrix} =
$$

$$
= \begin{bmatrix} -\alpha_X & \beta_X.(a_i(Y) + a_j(Y)).\bar{x}_i.(1 - \bar{x}_i) \\ \beta_Y.(b_i(X) + b_j(X)).\bar{y}_i.(1 - \bar{y}_i) & -\alpha_Y \end{bmatrix} \tag{2.18}
$$

Through Jacobian matrix (2.18) we identify where the interaction among agents is effectively present. Without any interaction, the elements of matrix $\mathbf{J}$ outside the main diagonal would be null, and as a result there would be no interdependence; the two equations could in such circumstance be analyzed separately. The interdependence implies that such elements have to be positive values, as long as we consider positive rewards generated by the fact that the other agent chooses precisely the same option.

The system under inspection is now system (2.19),

$$
\begin{bmatrix} \dot{x}_i(t) \\ \dot{y}_i(t) \end{bmatrix} = \mathbf{J}.\begin{bmatrix} x_i(t) - \bar{x}_i \\ y_i(t) - \bar{y}_i \end{bmatrix} \tag{2.19}
$$

As in section 2.3, the analysis of the dynamic system that is linearized in the neighborhood of the steady-state can be undertaken graphically, through the construction of a phase diagram, or analytically, through the computation of eigenvalues. Solving the characteristic equation one obtains,

$$\lambda_1, \lambda_2 = \frac{-(\alpha_X + \alpha_Y) \pm \sqrt{(\alpha_X - \alpha_Y)^2 + 4.j_{12}.j_{21}}}{2} \tag{2.20}$$

with

$$j_{12} = \beta_X.(a_i(Y) + a_j(Y)).\bar{x}_i.(1 - \bar{x}_i) \; ; \; j_{21} = \beta_Y.(b_i(X) + b_j(X)).\bar{y}_i.(1 - \bar{y}_i)$$

Given that j_{12} and j_{21} are positive values, the square root in expression (2.20) will be a real number. The dynamics of the system will differ according to each one of the following three cases:

1) $j_{12}.j_{21} < \alpha_X.\alpha_Y$;
2) $j_{12}.j_{21} = \alpha_X.\alpha_Y$;
3) $j_{12}.j_{21} > \alpha_X.\alpha_Y$.

In the first case, both eigenvalues are negative, what implies a situation of convergence towards a stable equilibrium. Thus, for relatively high levels of entropy the scenario of stability, which we have already found for the problem of the isolated agent, is again present. When the second of the above conditions holds, one of the eigenvalues will be equal to zero and the other one assumes a negative value: $\lambda_2 = -(\alpha_X + \alpha_Y)$; this will be an intermediate case in which the stable equilibrium exists but, in the phase diagram, convergence occurs following exclusively one of the axes. Finally, the third condition implies that one of the eigenvalues assumes a negative value, while the other will be a value above zero. This last case will correspond to a dynamic behavior characterized by a saddle-path equilibrium: there will be a unique stable trajectory, one-dimensional, through which the probability variables can eventually converge towards the steady-state.

In what follows, we graphically characterize each one of the eventual dynamic results of the model with interaction, resorting to phase diagrams.

The isoclines of the system can be determined by solving $\begin{bmatrix} \dot{x}_i(t) \\ \dot{y}_i(t) \end{bmatrix} = \begin{bmatrix} 0 \\ 0 \end{bmatrix}$. We find that

they are, respectively, $y_i(t) - \bar{y}_i = \dfrac{\alpha_X}{j_{12}}.[x_i(t) - \bar{x}_i]$ and $y_i(t) - \bar{y}_i = \dfrac{j_{21}}{\alpha_Y}.[x_i(t) - \bar{x}_i]$.

They both possess a positive slope, but in generic terms it is not possible to determine which of the lines is steeper.

Regard also the direction of the directional arrows. Since the element in the first row, first column of **J** is a negative value, the phase diagram will exhibit arrows pointing to the left at the right of $\dot{x}_i(t) = 0$, and arrows pointing to the right at the left of the same isocline. In a parallel way, since the element in the second row, first column of the Jacobian matrix is a positive value, we observe that to the right of the isocline $\dot{y}_i(t) = 0$ we can draw directional arrows pointing upwards, while to the left of this isocline, the directional arrows will be downward oriented.

In the first case, in which condition $j_{12}.j_{21} < \alpha_X.\alpha_Y$ holds, the slope of $\dot{x}_i(t) = 0$ is larger than the slope of $\dot{y}_i(t) = 0$. The direction of the directional arrows allows then to confirm the result of convergence: independently of the initial value of the probabilities, these converge to the corresponding steady-state value.

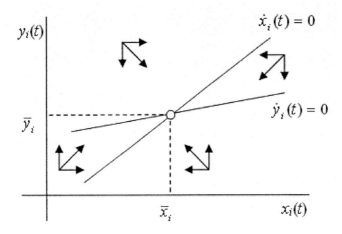

Figure 2.7. Phase diagram in the model of social interaction (stable equilibrium).

The second case, $j_{12}.j_{21} = \alpha_X.\alpha_Y$, will be a particular case, in which the slopes of the isoclines coincide. Given the expression of the isoclines, the coincidence in slopes also means that the two lines will share the exact same position. The corresponding phase diagram is given by figure 2.8. We emphasize that this is an intermediate case between the result of stability and the result of saddle-path equilibrium.

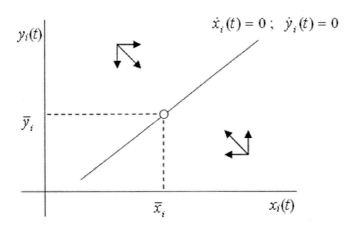

Figure 2.8. Phase diagram in the model of social interaction (with equal isoclines).

The saddle-path equilibrium is found when the condition $j_{12}.j_{21} > \alpha_X.\alpha_Y$ holds. With this condition, the slope $\dot{x}_i(t) = 0$ is smaller than the slope of $\dot{y}_i(t) = 0$ and the corresponding phase diagram takes the form presented in figure 2.9.

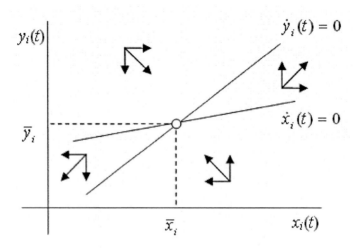

Figure 2.9. Phase diagram in the model of social interaction (saddle-path equilibrium).

Figure 2.9 adds some information to the one we have collected with the computation of the eigenvalues. We had noticed the existence of a saddle-point steady-state but we did not know the relative position of the stable and of the unstable trajectories. The stable trajectory, the one that allows for convergence towards the steady-state, will be according to the presented directional arrows negatively sloped. The unstable trajectory, the one that once followed makes the probabilities to depart from the equilibrium values, is positively sloped. Therefore, if in the vicinity of the equilibrium the system is over the stable trajectory, this means that convergence to the steady-state will occur with the probability of agent X choosing option i varying in the opposite direction of the probability of agent Y in choosing the same option i. Similarly, the interpretation of an unstable trajectory negatively sloped is that when the probability of one of the agents selecting option i tends to zero (to 1), the probability of the other agent choosing the same option also tends to zero (to 1).

The discussion in turn of social interaction has served essentially for one purpose: adding to the individual choices the interdependency in the decision making process. Despite the simplicity of the considered interaction component (we have simply assumed that the reward withdrawn from a choice increases by the fact that other individual will make exactly the same choice), we have noticed that by adding a new dimension to the model we have also added new dynamic features. The convergence to the long-run steady-state continues to be possible, however with interaction it is also possible a result of divergence and concentration of probability on a unique choice, even in the absence of a null value regarding the entropy component.

With social interaction it is simply necessary the product of the entropy values to remain below a given positive value $(j_{12}.j_{21})$, in order for the result of choice with certainty (probability 1) to be achieved.

This chapter has developed a dynamic model of learning / adaptation and entropy that has allowed characterizing the way in which the symbolic interaction among individuals – communication – has impact over the corresponding decision processes. We have pursued a generic analysis, where it was highlighted that a system without entropy produces certainty in choices, where we have found that learning is an important element in decision making but that does not necessarily change the dynamic characteristics of the theoretical structure, and where we have observed that social interaction, i.e., the scenario where the reward of a given choice is partially dependent of the choice of other agents, can introduce new elements into the analysis, namely in terms of variety of the possible dynamic outcomes.

2.5. APPLICATIONS

Application 1

Consider a model of binary choice (an agent chooses between action 1 and action 2). The following vector of parameters is known: $[\alpha\ \beta\ a_1\ a_2]=[0.5\ 1\ 1\ 2]$. The parameters have identical interpretation to the one presented in previous sections.

For the assumed vector of parameters,

a) Write the dynamic equation representing the temporal evolution of the variable probability of choice of option 1.
b) Present the steady-state values of the probabilities of choice referring to each option. In which circumstances is this equilibrium achieved?
c) Linearize the dynamic equation regarding the time change of the probability associated to the choice of option 1, in the vicinity of the steady-state. In which direction does this line shift when a positive change in the intensity of choice parameter occurs? And which is the direction followed by the line when there is a contraction on the value of parameter α?

The model of binary choice was developed in section 2.2. We have then determined the dynamic Equation (2.6), which translates the time evolution of the variable probability of choice of option 1, $x_1(t)$, and the corresponding steady-state, (2.7). We can resort to these expressions in order to answer the raised questions.

A. Write the Dynamic Equation

The required dynamic equation was computed in the text, where we have presented expression (2.6). Given the values of the memory parameter, of the intensity of choice and of the reward parameters, we conclude that the intertemporal change in the probability of choice corresponds to the rule

$$\frac{\dot{x}_1(t)}{x_1(t)} = \{-1-0.5.[\ln x_1(t)-\ln(1-x_1(t))]\}.[1-x_1(t)]$$

Observe that the expected reward associated to choice 2 is larger than the expected reward of choice 1 and for this reason the term of the equation relating to adaptation / learning will correspond to a lower than zero value.

B. Present the Steady-State Values

The equilibrium value of probability $x_1(t)$ is found in its generic form in (2.7). The steady-state value of probability $x_2(t)$ will be the difference between 1 and $x_1(t)$. Undertaking the corresponding computation:

$$\bar{x}_1 = \frac{e^{-2}}{1+e^{-2}} = 0.119\,;\; \bar{x}_2 = 1 - 0.119 = 0.881\,.$$

The expected reward associated to choice 2 is higher than the expected reward of choice 1. This is the reason why the equilibrium probability associated to choice 2 is a value significantly higher than the probability of choice of the first option. The probabilities do not assume the value zero (for option 1) and the value 1 (for option 2) because there exists a positive value of entropy; if $\alpha=0$ were eventually a true condition, then the choice would be made with total certainty; the probabilities would be 0 and 1 respectively.

If the memory parameter were a parameter with a value larger than 0.5, the level of choice uncertainty would be larger, i.e., the probability associated to the selection of option 1 would be higher and the probability associated to choice 2 would be lower, what would reveal increased difficulty in the decision making process. For instance, for $\alpha=2$ the following steady-state values are found,

$$\bar{x}_1 = \frac{e^{-0.5}}{1+e^{-0.5}} = 0.377\,;\; \bar{x}_2 = 1 - 0.377 = 0.623\,.$$

The above example allows observing that a faster loss of memory, which can be identified with a not so effective process of communication, makes the decision harder to undertake, since it makes the values of the probabilities of choice closer to each other. Increasing further the value of the memory loss parameter, one would observe that the probabilities of choice would converge to 0.5; in the limit case, when the memory loss value tends to infinity we would have equally probable options, and therefore the different expected rewards would be indistinguishable because the agent would be incapable of retaining through time the knowledge previously acquired about those differences regarding expected benefits.

The equilibrium value is achieved for any positive value of the memory loss parameter. We have verified in section 2.2 that the steady-state is stable: independently of the initial values of the probabilities of choice there is a tendency for these to follow a convergence process in the direction of the long-run steady-state point.

C. Linearize the Dynamic Equation

The linearization of the dynamic equation involves the computation of the derivative $\dfrac{\partial \dot{x}_1(t)}{\partial x_1(t)}$, and corresponding evaluation in the steady-state point. From the computation of the derivative we obtain the expression $-0.5 + \{-1 - 0.5.[\ln x_1(t) - \ln(1 - x_1(t))]\}.[1 - 2.x_1(t)]$; evaluating this expression in the steady-state we find the slope of the linearized equation, which corresponds to the symmetric value of the constant of memory loss.

The generic expression of the linearized equation is $\dot{x}_1(t) = -\alpha.[x_1(t) - \bar{x}_1]$. Having in consideration the value of the memory parameter and the equilibrium value found in the previous answer, the required expression will be: $\dot{x}_1(t) = 0.03 - 0.5.x_1(t)$.

Given a positive change in the parameter of intensity of choice, the slope of the linearized equation will not change (this will simply be determined by the constant of memory). However, there will occur a parallel shift of the line in consideration; an increase in the value of β implies a fall in the steady-state value of the probability of choice 1, since $a_1 < a_2$ (if the opposite condition was verified, an increase in the value of the intensity of choice would have as a consequence a positive change in the steady-state value of x_1). If the steady-state value falls, then the point in the vertical axis of the considered line will be a value lower than 0.03 and thus, for this reason, the linearized equation will suffer a parallel shift to the left.

If the value of the parameter α suffers a negative change, then the slope of the linear equation will also suffer a change; this will decrease to an amount that in absolute value is lower than 0.5. The modification in the value of the memory loss parameter has also a consequence over the steady-state value of $x_1(t)$; in the specific case, a fall in the value of α implies that the decisions will involve a larger degree of certainty and therefore the probabilities of choice will tend to their extreme values; since the probability associated to option 1 is the lowest of the two, a fall in α implies an approximation of this probability value towards zero. In this specific circumstance, the equilibrium value diminishes and, consequently, the point in the vertical axis, which is given by the product between the entropy parameter and the equilibrium value, will also fall. The new straight line will then have a value in the vertical axis lower than 0.03 and a slope below 0.5 in absolute value. The shift in the linearized dynamic equation is plotted in the displayed figure.

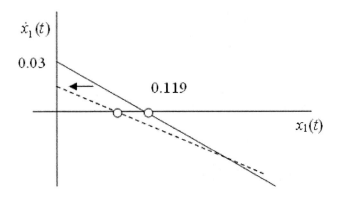

In the figure, the non dashed line represents the linearized equation before the perturbation and the dashed line will be the one that originates in the reduction of the value of the memory loss parameter. Observe that there is a fall in the steady-state value of the probability of choice of the option that is being considered; this will imply, in the vicinity of the steady-state, a shift of the line to the left. However, the line will not migrate to the left in all its extension because the movement is not a parallel one; the slope of the line, which coincides in absolute value with the parameter of memory loss, will also suffer a change.

Application 2

Recover the model with learning dynamics of section 2.3. Discuss, for this analytical structure, the impact of a positive variation over the value of a_j.

In section 2.3 we have included in the analytical structure regarding adaptation and entropy, a dynamic equation representing the time evolution of the intensity of choice. With Equation (2.8) we have intended to pass the idea that the way in which a given agent reacts to the accumulation of results relating different choice alternatives does not have to be an unchangeable process.

The intensity of choice tends to grow positively in time because the communication process allows the agent to learn and thus to gain a capacity of faster adaptation to expected rewards. We have also assumed that the ability to learn is limited, i.e., as the intensity of choice rises, the corresponding marginal increases tend to be progressively smaller.

Under this scenario, we have found steady-state values and we have characterized the dynamics of the model. The constant steady-state value of the intensity of choice depends solely on a set of parameters associated to the respective temporal evolution. In turn, the equilibrium value of the ratio between any two probabilities $x_i(t)$ and $x_j(t)$ will depend on the equilibrium value of the intensity of choice, on the parameter of memory loss and also on the expected rewards. Therefore, given a positive change on the value of the reward associated with the choice j, a_j, the steady-state value of the ratio $\phi(t)$ will decrease, as one would expect: if the value of the reward associated to option j increases, then the ratio between probabilities of choice of options i and j will become a lower value.

In what concerns the dynamics of convergence towards the steady-state, a larger reward a_j does not produce any effect over the qualitative nature of the dynamics of the model: we continue to have a stable equilibrium, what implies that independently of the location of the initial state $[\beta(0), \phi(0)]$, there is a process of convergence towards the steady-state as characterized above. Although the stable nature of the model is maintained, the position of one of the isoclines in the respective phase diagram will change. Given Jacobian matrix (2.11), one observes that the element in the second row, first column will change its value, what provokes a change in the slope of the isocline $\dot{\phi}(t) = 0$.

To graphically translate the effect of an increase on reward a_j, we consider that condition $\alpha > 1 - b$ holds and that at the start, before the perturbation, the inequality $a_j > a_i$ is observed. In this case, the slope of the isocline $\dot{\phi}(t) = 0$ will be negative and the more negative it will be as the reward associated to option j increases. To proceed with the representation of the phase diagram, it is necessary to account for the previous reasoning:

- on one hand, the assumed perturbation changes the equilibrium value of the ratio $\phi(t)$ in the direction of a lower value;
- on the other hand, given the considered constraints, the slope of the line $\dot{\phi}(t) = 0$ is reduced in absolute value, assuming that initially it is already negative.

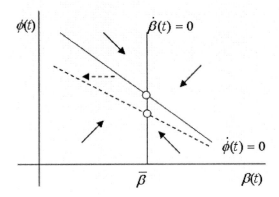

In the presented phase diagram, one can observe that the result of stability is maintained, and the changes occur essentially at the level of the position of the steady-state point (which will be the point closer to the horizontal axis of the two points presented over line $\dot{\beta}(t) = 0$) and at the level of line $\dot{\phi}(t) = 0$, that serves as a reference to understand the position of the directional arrows; the new isocline, after the perturbation, is the dashed one.

Application 3

For the scenario of social interaction of section 2.4 the following elements are known:
$a_i=5$; $a_j=2$; $a_i(Y)=1$; $a_j(Y)=1$; $b_i=2$; $b_j=2$; $b_i(X)=0.2$; $b_j(X)=0.5$; $\bar{y}_i = 0.25$; $\gamma \equiv \alpha_X = \alpha_Y = \beta_X = \beta_Y > 0$.

Having in consideration the presented values and conditions,

a) Determine the steady-state value of the probability of agent X choosing option i;
b) Simplify the Jacobian matrix in (2.18);
c) Characterize the dynamics of the model, through the computation of the eigenvalues;
d) Characterize the dynamics of the model, through the construction of a phase diagram;
e) Evaluate the effect, over the model's dynamics, of the change in the value of the reward of agent Y when agent X chooses option i; this change modifies the corresponding value of $b_i(X)=0.2$ to $b_i(X)=1.2$ (consider also that this change does not modify the steady-state value of probability $y_i(t)$).

A. Determining the Steady State Value

In the scenario of social interaction, we consider a theoretical structure of binary choice, that allows for alternatives i and j. The equations representing the motion in time of the probabilities of choice of option i, for two agents, X and Y, have been computed and presented under the form of expressions (2.16) and (2.17).

The fundamental and distinctive characteristic of the equations relating to the choice probabilities with interaction, relatively to the scenario where interaction is absent, respects to the fact that the benefit associated to the choice of an option i by a given agent will depend, partially, on the choice undertaken by the other agent. Therefore, the choice becomes interactive: the process of communication does not serve solely to form an evaluation concerning eventual possibilities of choice, becoming also a process in which an action of some players has direct impact over the decisions made by others.

To determine the steady-state value of the probability of agent X choosing alternative i, we resort to Equation (2.16). Taking in consideration the condition $\dot{x}_i(t) = 0$ we will encounter the following result:

$$\overline{x}_i = \frac{e^{\frac{\beta_X}{\alpha_X}.\left[a_i - a_j - a_j(Y) + (a_i(Y) + a_j(Y)).\overline{y}_i\right]}}{1 + e^{\frac{\beta_X}{\alpha_X}.\left[a_i - a_j - a_j(Y) + (a_i(Y) + a_j(Y)).\overline{y}_i\right]}}.$$

The obtained steady-state expression can be simplified by taking in consideration the values and conditions of the exercise. One observes that the requested equilibrium value is $\overline{x}_i = \frac{e^{1.5}}{1 + e^{1.5}} = 0.818$. The high value of the steady-state probability reflects the notion that to alternative i is associated, for agent X, an expected reward that is higher than the expected reward associated to action j.

B. Simplify the Jacobian Matrix

The matrix in (2.18) is the result of linearizing the system of equations corresponding to the evolution of the probability of choice of option i for agents X and Y. With the presented numerical values and with the steady-state value computed above, this matrix simplifies to

$$\mathbf{J} = \begin{bmatrix} -\gamma & 0.298.\gamma \\ 0.131.\gamma & -\gamma \end{bmatrix}.$$

C. Computation of the Eigenvalues

For the computed $\mathbf{J}$ matrix, the following trace and determinant are found: $Tr(\mathbf{J}) = -2.\gamma$ and $Det(\mathbf{J}) = 0.961.\gamma^2$. The eigenvalues associated to matrix $\mathbf{J}$ are determined by solving the following characteristic equation: $\lambda^2 + 2.\gamma.\lambda + 0.961.\gamma = 0$. The determined values are $\lambda_1, \lambda_2 = (-1 \pm \sqrt{0.156}/2).\gamma$, i.e., $\lambda_1 = -1.197.\gamma$ and $\lambda_2 = -0.802.\gamma$. Since $\gamma > 0$, one concludes that both eigenvalues have negative sign and therefore the system is stable: there is a tendency for the convergence of the probability variables in the direction of the corresponding long-run equilibrium values.

D. Construction of a Phase Diagram

The graphical analysis should confirm the dynamic result that the computation of the eigenvalues has revealed. Specifically, one should be able to verify the existence of a stable steady-state; for any initial value of the probabilities associated to the choice option i for each one of the two assumed agents, the dynamic adjustment will consist on a convergence process of the probabilities towards the corresponding equilibrium values.

To build the phase diagram we begin by finding the expressions of the isoclines,

$$\begin{bmatrix} \dot{x}_i(t) \\ \dot{y}_i(t) \end{bmatrix} = \begin{bmatrix} 0 \\ 0 \end{bmatrix} \Rightarrow \begin{cases} y_i(t) - \overline{y}_i = \dfrac{\gamma}{0.298.\gamma}.\left[x_i(t) - \overline{x}_i \right] \\[4mm] y_i(t) - \overline{y}_i = \dfrac{0.131.\gamma}{\gamma}.\left[x_i(t) - \overline{x}_i \right] \end{cases}$$

Given the steady-state value of $y_i(t)$, presented with the application, and the steady-state value of $x_i(t)$, computed in the first part of the exercise, the isoclines will simplify to i) $y_i(t) = -2.495 + 3.356.x_i(t)$; and (ii) $y_i(t) = 0.143 + 0.131.x_i(t)$. The line $\dot{x}_i(t) = 0$ has a larger slope than $\dot{y}_i(t) = 0$, what allows obtaining a specific result that is similar to the one for the generic case in figure 2.7.

The element in the first row, first column of the Jacobian matrix is negative what allows to present horizontal directional arrows converging to the corresponding isocline; the element in the second row, first column is a positive value and therefore the vertical directional arrows will also translate a convergence towards the second isocline. As a result of the described dynamic motion, there will be convergence towards the steady-state or, in other words, the equilibrium point is stable. In the following figure the phase diagram in figure 2.7 is presented for the specific case we are dealing with.

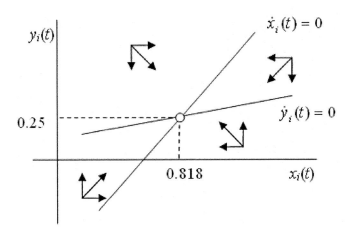

E. Evaluate the Effect

To evaluate the effect of a change in the value of one of the parameters of reward, one needs to re-compute Jacobian matrix (2.18). In particular, the element in the second row, first line will be the one that will suffer a change. Now, we observe that

$$\beta_Y.(b_i(X)+b_j(X)).\bar{y}_i.(1-\bar{y}_i) = \gamma.(1.2+0.5).(0.25).(0.75) = 0.319.\gamma .$$

With this change in matrix **J**, the eigenvalues that can be computed will assume distinct values relatively to the ones previously obtained. The eigenvalues are now the result of solving equation $\lambda^2 + 2.\gamma.\lambda + 0.905.\gamma = 0$. The computation of the eigenvalues leads, then, to $\lambda_1 = -1.308.\gamma$ and $\lambda_2 = -0.692.\gamma$. There is a change in value of the eigenvalues, but they remain both negative; then, one concludes that the type of dynamics of the model will not be modified, i.e., the stable equilibrium result is once again obtained, although there is a significant increase in the benefit withdrawn by agent Y in the choice of option i, when the option of agent X is the same.

Chapter 3

OPTIMIZATION OF THE COMMUNICATION RESULT

In chapter 2 we have analyzed how communication influences choices. To take a decision it is necessary to know the expected reward associated to each alternative and to understand that there are factors that transform such expected rewards into decisions taken with a high or with a low degree of certainty. Specifically, the loss of memory or the capacity to valuate new data related with expected rewards, are factors that the decision making process needs to consider.

Therefore, until now the communication process has remained inside a black box: communication is, in the perspective of chapter 2, a process through which one acquires beliefs about the expected outcome of certain actions, knowing that the degree in which those expected rewards are apprehended and forgotten can vary in time or among individuals. The communication process in itself is not analyzed; in particular, the causes triggering expected rewards are not explored, they just arise exogenously.

The full understanding of the communication process requires more than accepting it is the vehicle leading to the knowledge needed to the decision making. It is central to understand how the expected rewards are generated, and to include in this explanation some optimization process, through which the agents involved in the communication process emerge with a well defined goal: the maximization of the expected reward.

This is a relevant difference between the analysis in the last chapter and the one we undertake in this one. In the present case, we consider an optimization setting, where communication is managed in order to obtain the best possible result. An optimization structure requires the acknowledgment of a trade-off that one needs to address: communication generates benefits, solving inefficiencies at the level of information asymmetries among different agents, but it also has costs, in the sense that it consumes resources of various types (cognitive resources, time resources and resources associated with sending and processing information). According to this view, communication models should be able to make an optimal or efficient evaluation of the resources available to communicate. This is the path that the present chapter follows. It is also the setup in which Forges (1986, 1990), Myerson (1986), Bárány (1992), Urbano and Villa (2002), Ben-Porath (2003) and Gossner, Hernández and Neyman (2006) develop the study of the optimal allocation of communication resources and approach the notion of communication equilibrium.

Once again, we highlight the impossibility of having a single model capable of providing an exhaustive and complete explanation of the complex process of communication. Thus, some compromises are required and several simplifications need to be considered. The model to develop in this chapter is a model of endogenous rewards, i.e., one intends to characterize the way in which the optimizing behavior of a given agent leads to a given time trajectory for the expected benefit associated to a given choice.

The first simplification to take into account consists in considering a single action. For this, some agent will undertake a process of symbolic interaction with third parties in order to collect knowledge, information and some emotional data (about desires, tastes, fears, i.e., about others' behavior in general) that allow to maximize the expected reward of the behavior to adopt.

It is a model of allocation of cognitive resources. This means that the agent is endowed with a certain capacity of reasoning and evaluation relatively to some problem that she faces; this capacity corresponds to the cognitive resources allocated to a given process of evaluation and choice. Continuing to consider a dynamic scenario, we assume that the cognitive resources are not constant over time; instead, they evolve in time according to a given rule which will indicate that the larger is the quantity of cognitive resources already associated with analyzing a given alternative, the stronger will be the tendency to continue to associate resources to such task.

The cognitive resources may have two uses. They are used in the symbolic interaction with third parties with the purpose of enlarging the stock of such resources, what allows the potential capacity to choose to grow further. Or, alternatively, the resources are withdrawn from the communication process and associated to an introspective activity of information processing and evaluation of alternatives. The expected benefit, in turn, will be as higher as the larger is the quantity of resources diverted from the communication process and in the direction of weighting different choices.

Hence, we have a conflicting process: the capacity to evaluate and choose (which is translated on the capacity to attribute a high expected value to the reward associated to the action that will be undertaken) is stimulated by the process of communicating with others, however the act of decision making is independent of the communication process and it leads to the waste of resources that will no longer exist in order to increase the stock of accumulated cognitive resources.

The dilemma of the agent involved in the communication process is then the following: at each time moment, the agent has to allocate a share of the cognitive resources to decide and undertake choices, i.e., she has to attribute some kind of classification to the option she faces in order to maximize the expected value of the reward that her action will produce. The other share of the cognitive resources will be allocated to the accumulation of new cognitive resources and this accumulation is done through communication: sending and receiving messages, creating and obtaining feedback, i.e., through interaction. The dilemma relates to the fact that the agent cannot allocate the same cognitive resources to both functions. A given share of cognitive resources, in some moment in time, can only have one use: to communicate or to weight options with the purpose of maximizing the outcome of the choice.

As in chapter 2, the elaboration of a model that is limited to establishing relations between some relevant variables in the communication process implies an excessive simplification of reality, which is close to an explanation of the hypodermic needle type. However, the model in this chapter achieves more than the simple presentation of the communication process as a one-directional act of message sending. The interaction process is now implicit in the analysis; our model's representative agent does not have to be necessarily just a receiver of messages, but someone that through a maximizing behavior searches to withdraw the highest possible benefit from the interaction using communication. Achieving to collect cognitive resources allowing to make a choice with the highest possible expected result requires information exchange, the generation of knowledge and the sharing of experiences and feelings, and not only a passive attitude of accepting the contents of the messages transmitted by third agents.

Consequently, even though the model to develop reveals limitations in terms of explaining capacities, it should be understood as a description of a dynamic process in which an agent, which has the possibility to communicate with others in a systematic way, possesses a decision capacity over the mode in which, in each time moment, she employs the available resources: by collecting data that adds value to the capacity to evaluate and decide (by communicating) or by proceeding to an evaluation of the alternatives of choice in order to maximize the expected benefit of the undertaken action.

The chapter is organized in the following way. Section 3.1 formalizes the model of optimization of the reward provided by the communication process. Section 3.2 undertakes an analysis of the model, computing optimality conditions and studying the stability of the steady-state. Sections 3.3 and 3.4 are destined to the consideration of more sophisticated versions of the model. Section 3.3 considers social interaction; in the present context, social interaction implies that the cognitive capacity of others has a relevant impact over the growth of the cognitive resources available to the individual agent; section 3.4 assumes a scenario where communication efficiency varies in time.

Finally, in section 3.5 we discuss some applications relating the developed theoretical structure.

3.1. A MODEL OF ALLOCATION OF COGNITIVE RESOURCES

Communication generates and transmits knowledge, information, emotions and feelings that are not easy to translate into a small set of variables. Nevertheless, in this section we intend to conceive a simple mechanism destined to the understanding of the relation between communication and expected rewards relating to possible behavior options.

We begin by assuming that in some initial moment, $t=0$, an agent employs a given quantity of cognitive resources $k(0)$ in order to obtain an expected result or reward associated with a given problem relatively to which the agent has to make decisions through time. Variable $k(t)$ will translate, in each moment of time, the resources that the agent has associated to the issue at hand; these resources can be used in two different ways:

- • - the development of interaction through communication: this interaction will have the purpose of adding value to the cognitive resources already available; thus, $k(t)$ grows with communication. In other words, communication will be a process of investment that allows accumulating value to the cognitive resources associated to the problem in turn of which the communication process takes place;
- • evaluation of alternatives, with the objective of choosing the behavior that maximizes the expected benefit for the agent. Variable $z(t)$ will translate the amount of cognitive resources deviated from communication to the evaluation of choices and information

processing. The higher the value of this variable, the larger will be the benefit that the agent can expect, i.e., additional resources associated to the evaluation process will imply the possibility of achieving a better expected reward.

We now need to put in formal terms the ideas concerning the way in which the employment of cognitive resources to communication adds value to such resources and about the way in which the diversion of resources away from communication allows to evaluate options and to make the expected benefits to grow. In what concerns the accumulation of cognitive resources, it is reasonable to assume a function that transforms, through communication, cognitive resources into an additional quantity of these resources; letting $y(t)$ be the amount of cognitive resources obtained through the employment of a quantity of resources $k(t)$ on a communication process, consider the following function,

$$y(t) = A.k(t)^{\zeta} \tag{3.1}$$

Function (3.1) should be interpreted in the following way: if in a given communication relation one employs a quantity of cognitive resources $k(t)$, the final outcome in terms of cognitive resources will be a value $y(t)$, that will depend on the parameters of the function; $A>0$ is a parameter of efficiency of the communication process, i.e., the higher is the value of this parameter, the more capable will be the agent in transforming cognitive resources into additional cognitive resources. The efficiency in the communication process is not something that is easy to measure or evaluate; this efficiency will depend on the characteristics and capacity of the agent, but it is also a variable that suffers exogenous pressures, in the sense that it depends on the other players in the communication process, on the used channels and means and on the existence of a given quantity of noise that is associated to the process.

Constant $0<\zeta<1$ reflects the limits of the communication capacity in terms of making cognitive resources to grow. Function (3.1) is concave, what is an indication that there are decreasing marginal returns associated to communication: the potential of communication in making the individual's cognitive resources to grow becomes progressively smaller with the quantity of resources already accumulated. Above some limit value, communication becomes asymptotically redundant: the increase in cognition that the communication involvement generates becomes negligible.

In what concerns variable $z(t)$, this represents the amount of cognitive resources that at each time moment are withdrawn from the communication process, in order to be used in the process of decision making. It will be necessary, then, to establish a relation between this variable and the expected reward of the action that predictably will be taken. This relation is expressed in the following function,

$$z(t) = e^{a(t)} \tag{3.2}$$

With expression (3.2) one takes increasing returns in the utilization of cognitive returns to evaluate choices. Being function (3.2) an increasing and convex function, the progressive use of resources on the effort concerning decision making will contribute positively and in an increasing way to achieve a better result. In other words, the larger the quantity of resources employed in processing information and evaluating choices, the faster the expected reward of the choice will rise. In reality, for different choices function (3.2) can assume multiple forms; in what concerns our modelling structure we will resort to the mentioned assumption: additional resources allocated to the decision process contribute in an exponential way for the growth of the obtainable reward.

Having presented expressions (3.1) and (3.2), it is possible to define a dynamic equation representing the accumulation of cognitive resources. According with (3.3), the variation on the stock of cognitive resources will correspond to the difference between the value of the already accumulated resources, generated by the communication process, and the value of the resources diverted from the communication process into the evaluation of choices. We consider as well a term of depreciation or obsolescence of the cognitive resources held; specifically, we assume a rate of depreciation of the cognitive resources associated with the considered communication and decision process that is equal to $\delta_k > 0$. Therefore,

$$\dot{k}(t) = y(t) - z(t) - \delta_k . k(t) \Rightarrow$$
$$\dot{k}(t) = A.k(t)^\zeta - e^{a(t)} - \delta_k . k(t), \quad k(0) = k_0 \text{ given.} \tag{3.3}$$

Differential Equation (3.3) works as a resource constraint, i.e., it is a kind of frontier of cognitive possibilities; this frontier is not static, evolving in time according with the above rule. At each time moment, there exists a quantity of cognitive resources, generated by the communication process (that in turn is fed by these resources), from which one needs to withdraw a share in order to evaluate choices with the goal of obtaining some benefit. Another share of such resources is lost by simple obsolescence.

Now that we have characterized the constraint the agent faces in her task of attributing a value to the decision that will eventually be taken, one needs to look at the maximization problem. The agent will try to maximize the expected reward of the action under evaluation. However, this maximization process will not be static as well. One assumes that the agent is taking her decisions today, at time $t=0$, with consequences that spread into the future, given some specified horizon; thus, she must try to solve an optimization problem in the present but accounting not only for the present benefit but for the set of all the expected benefits of all the subsequent time moments.

As it is obvious, the individual that is involved in the communication and decision process will not weight in the same way present rewards and rewards that are achievable in some future moments. The consideration of a discount rate is required, $\rho > 0$. With the discount rate, the agent weights results as a function of the distance relatively to the present moment; the far in time are the considered benefits, less weight such expected benefits will have in the intertemporal problem that the agent intends to solve.

The problem of the representative agent consists in the maximization of the sum of all the expected rewards in time, with the future rewards being discounted as a function of the distance relatively to the present moment,

$$Max \int_0^{+\infty} a(t).e^{-\rho.t} .dt \tag{3.4}$$

In the optimization problem (3.4) we assume an infinite horizon, i.e., we assume that the benefits of the communication and choice process are weighted without considering a defined time limit, what makes sense once we consider the discount rate; asymptotically, after a given time moment the relevance attributed to the future rewards becomes negligible (note that $\lim\limits_{t\to\infty} e^{-\rho.t} = 0$).

With (3.3) and (3.4), we have put together the ingredients needed to study the way in which the allocation of cognitive resources to communication and to the decision making generates an optimal result to the agent. The problem of the agent will be the intertemporal maximization of the expected benefit, with this being a not completely free maximization; it is constrained by a cognitive resource restriction, (3.3), according to which the cognitive resources only grow, allowing obtaining better results, if the communication process is perpetuated.

In section 3.2 we solve the model. In particular, we intend to find a set of optimality conditions, based on which one may undertake a dynamic analysis regarding the relation between expected benefit and the accumulation of cognitive resources.

3.2. OPTIMALITY CONDITIONS AND DYNAMIC ANALYSIS

In this section, we solve the optimal control problem (3.4), which is subject to the cognitive resources frontier (3.3). Te first step in solving the model consists in the presentation of a current value Hamiltonian function that takes the following form,

$$\aleph(t) = a(t) + p(t).\left[A.k(t)^{\varsigma} - e^{a(t)} - \delta_k.k(t)\right] \tag{3.5}$$

In (3.5), variable $p(t)$ will correspond to a co-state or shadow-price variable of variable $k(t)$. The Hamiltonian function allows obtaining the optimality conditions. The first-order optimality conditions of the problem are:

$$\aleph_a = 0 \Rightarrow 1 = p(t).e^{a(t)} \Rightarrow a(t) = -\ln p(t) \tag{3.6}$$

$$\dot{p}(t) = \left[\rho - \varsigma.A.k(t)^{-(1-\varsigma)} + \delta_k\right]p(t) \tag{3.7}$$

$$\lim\limits_{t\to\infty} p(t).e^{-\rho.t}.k(t) = 0 \quad \text{(transversality condition)} \tag{3.8}$$

Relations (3.6) and (3.7) hold in the circumstance in which the cognitive resources are being used in order to maximize the future flow of expected benefits. From these relations one withdraws a dynamic equation corresponding to the optimal time evolution of the expected reward variable. In order to obtain this, we differentiate (3.6) with respect to time, what allows to obtain the relation $\dot{a}(t) = -\dot{p}(t)/p(t)$. Replacing the growth rate of the co-state variable in (3.7) by the symmetric of the time variation of the benefit variable, one obtains

$$\dot{a}(t) = \zeta.A.k(t)^{-(1-\zeta)} - (\rho + \delta_k) \tag{3.9}$$

The dynamics of the model may be interpreted taking in consideration the system of equations formed by (3.3) and (3.9). In this system the endogenous variables are the stock of cognitive resources, $k(t)$ and the benefit produced by the decision, $a(t)$. The first is a state variable, in the sense that it is deterministically determined by the process of communication and information processing; the second is a control variable, because it is directly obtained from the variable that in this framework is subject to control: variable $z(t)$, which, we recall, represents the resources that in each time moment the agent decides to divert from the communication process in order to process information and evaluate the results of the decision to undertake.

This system of equations, besides containing two endogenous variables, involves also the assumption of four parameters, which will influence the considered optimization problem. These are, we recall, the discount rate relating the future expected benefits (ρ), the depreciation rate of the cognitive resources (δ_k), the parameter of communication competence (A), and the constant representing the decreasing returns of communication on the accumulation of cognitive resources (ζ).

A first step for the understanding of the assumed dynamic process, consists in the evaluation of the long-term result. The long-run steady-state is defined as the setting in which the variables in the model will no longer vary. Solving the system $\left[\dot{k}(t), \dot{a}(t)\right] = (0,0)$, we find the steady-state values of the two variables. These are,

$$\bar{k} = \left(\frac{\zeta.A}{\rho + \delta_k}\right)^{1/(1-\zeta)} ; \quad \bar{a} = \ln\left[\left(\frac{\rho}{\zeta} + \frac{1-\zeta}{\zeta}.\delta_k\right)\left(\frac{\zeta.A}{\rho + \delta_k}\right)^{1/(1-\zeta)}\right] \tag{3.10}$$

The steady-state result in (3.10) indicates that the long-run values of both variables correspond to a unique point, i.e., there is a single possible long-run result relatively to which the communication process result will converge or diverge, depending on the stability properties of the derived system. Divergence will imply, in this case, to follow in the direction of absence of communication and, as a result, the impossibility of accumulating resources allowing to perpetuate the process of choice evaluation.

To understand in which circumstances the variables of the model converge or diverge relatively to the steady-state point (3.10) it becomes necessary to pursue a dynamic analysis similar to the one developed in chapter 2. Two alternatives are possible: the graphical analysis resorting to a phase diagram, and the analytical study which implies the computation of the eigenvalues of the Jacobian matrix associated to the linearized system. Let us begin by presenting the phase diagram.

In a first moment, we need to determine the Jacobian matrix associated with system (3.3)-(3.9). Once computed the Jacobian matrix, one can present a linearized version of the model in the vicinity of the steady-state. The computation leads to

$$J = \begin{bmatrix} \left.\dfrac{\partial \dot{k}(t)}{\partial k(t)}\right|_{(\bar{k},\bar{a})} & \left.\dfrac{\partial \dot{k}(t)}{\partial a(t)}\right|_{(\bar{k},\bar{a})} \\ \left.\dfrac{\partial \dot{a}(t)}{\partial k(t)}\right|_{(\bar{k},\bar{a})} & \left.\dfrac{\partial \dot{a}(t)}{\partial a(t)}\right|_{(\bar{k},\bar{a})} \end{bmatrix} = \begin{bmatrix} \rho & -e^{\bar{a}} \\ -(1-\zeta).\dfrac{\rho+\delta_k}{\bar{k}} & 0 \end{bmatrix} \qquad (3.11)$$

For the linearized system, the isoclines (lines of absence of time evolution for each one of the variables) are easily found,

$$\dot{k}(t) = 0 \Rightarrow a(t) - \bar{a} = \frac{\rho}{e^{\bar{a}}}.[k(t) - \bar{k}];$$

$$\dot{a}(t) = 0 \Rightarrow k(t) = \bar{k}.$$

In the referential $[k(t),a(t)]$, the first isocline displays a positive slope, while the second will be a vertical line. The Jacobian matrix furnishes also indications about the orientation of the directional arrows; since $\left.\dfrac{\partial \dot{k}(t)}{\partial k(t)}\right|_{(\bar{k},\bar{a})} = \rho > 0$, the flows horizontally represented, which

have as reference the isocline $\dot{k}(t) = 0$, will reveal divergence relatively to the corresponding isocline; since $\left.\dfrac{\partial \dot{a}(t)}{\partial k(t)}\right|_{(\bar{k},\bar{a})} = -(1-\zeta).\dfrac{\rho+\delta_k}{\bar{k}} < 0$, the directional arrows

respecting to the time evolution of variable $a(t)$, vertically presented, will display a downward direction to the right of the corresponding isocline and an upward direction to the left of such line. The above information concerning the directional arrows allows building the phase diagram of figure 3.1; the diagram also allows for a straightforward perception of the type of dynamics that is associated to the model.

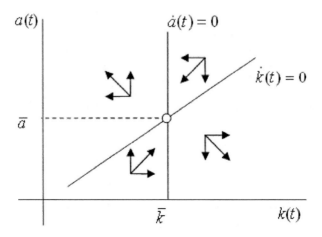

Figure 3.1. Phase diagram for the model of optimization of the communication result.

Figure 3.1 reveals the existence of a saddle-path stable equilibrium. We identify two trajectories that may alternatively be followed, depending on the initial values of the model's variables: a stable trajectory possessing a positive slope, and an unstable trajectory with a negative slope. If the unstable trajectory is followed, the system tends to a long-run solution where no communication is possible and all the resources are channelled to the treatment of information or to the decision making process, or on the contrary, to a solution in which communication is maximized leaving no resources left to be allocated to the decision making process.

The most common result will be the one in which, starting from the initial state in which cognitive resources relating the decision process are relatively low and in which the expected benefit of the process is also relatively low because few resources can be allocated to the decision process, i.e., $\left[k(0), a(0)\right] < (\overline{k}, \overline{a})$, the system converges following the stable trajectory in an upward direction: communication intensifies, giving place to a larger quantity of resources that help to create stronger beliefs regarding the problem at hand, making in this way the expected benefit to grow.

The saddle-path stable equilibrium result can also be achieved through resorting to the computation of the eigenvalues of the Jacobian matrix. Observing that $Tr(J)=\rho$ and that

$$Det(J) = -(1-\zeta).\frac{\rho+\delta_k}{\overline{k}}.e^{\overline{a}}$$, then, representing the eigenvalues by λ_1 and λ_2, and resorting

to the matrix calculus rule under which $Tr(J)= \lambda_1+\lambda_2$ and $Det(J)= \lambda_1.\lambda_2$, it is straightforward to observe that one of the eigenvalues is negative while the other is positive, what allows for a confirmation of the saddle-path stability result.

Under this equilibrium, there will be a convergence trajectory of positive slope that once followed by the variables indicates that the cognitive resources and the expected benefit evolve in a same direction, or, in other words, communication process and cognitive resources used to generate choice rewards converge to an equilibrium result through a process of mutual reinforcement.

The saddle trajectory or stable trajectory can be presented in analytical terms. For such, we need to compute the eigenvector associated to the negative eigenvalue (let this be λ_1). This vector includes elements p_{11} and p_{21}, which obey to the following condition:

$(\rho - \lambda_1).p_{11} - e^{\overline{a}}.p_{21} = 0$. Considering $p_{21}=1$, one will have $p_{11} = \dfrac{e^{\overline{a}}}{\rho - \lambda_1}$, which will be a

positive value, given the sign of the eigenvalue.

The stable trajectory will be a straight line that goes through the steady-state point (as it is obvious, a line over which variables converge to the steady-state has to pass through this point) and with a slope given by the ratio of the elements of the eigenvector associated to the negative eigenvalue. Specifically, the following expression will correspond to the stable

trajectory on its generic form: $a(t) - \overline{a} = \dfrac{p_{21}}{p_{11}}.\left[k(t) - \overline{k}\right]$. Given the computed eigenvector,

the stable trajectory is:

$$a(t) = \bar{a} - (\rho - \lambda_1) . \frac{\bar{k}}{e^{\bar{a}}} + \frac{\rho - \lambda_1}{e^{\bar{a}}} . k(t) \qquad (3.12)$$

The relation in (3.12) involves a positive slope, what confirms the results from the graphical analysis. Note that, according to figure 3.1, the slope of the saddle trajectory has to be larger than the slope of the isocline $\dot{k}(t) = 0$. Observing the value of both slopes we confirm this result: in (3.12), the slope is larger than the one of the mentioned isocline in an amount $-\lambda_1 / e^{\bar{a}}$.

The built model has characterized the way in which the communication process can be used to generate benefits. By confronting communication as a means to acquire evaluation skills and the need to use such skills to weight alternatives in order to obtain the highest possible expected result, we have understood that there exists a steady-state to which the variables of the model converge evolving in the same direction and following the stable trajectory.

Assuming that the stable trajectory is effectively followed, the dynamic analysis can be further developed through the study of the impact of the variation in the value of each one of the parameters, in order to understand how the long-run equilibrium and the dynamic evolution in the direction of such equilibrium can be disturbed.

Consider the following vector of exogenous perturbations:

Matrix $J(X)$ identifies the impact over each one of the equations of a change in the value of each of three parameters: the rate at which future benefits are discounted, the depreciation rate of the cognitive resources and the parameter representing the efficiency of the communication process. The impact of the variation in the value of each one of these parameters over the steady-state is two-fold: there is a short-run effect, which consists on the immediate jump of the system in the direction of a new stable trajectory, and in a second moment a process of adjustment following a new stable trajectory that culminates in the achievement of the new steady-state point, the one that will hold in the post-perturbation scenario.

$$J(X) = \begin{bmatrix} \dfrac{\partial \dot{k}(t)}{\partial \rho(t)}\bigg|_{(\bar{k},\bar{a})} & \dfrac{\partial \dot{k}(t)}{\partial \delta_k(t)}\bigg|_{(\bar{k},\bar{a})} & \dfrac{\partial \dot{k}(t)}{\partial A(t)}\bigg|_{(\bar{k},\bar{a})} \\[3mm] \dfrac{\partial \dot{a}(t)}{\partial \rho(t)}\bigg|_{(\bar{k},\bar{a})} & \dfrac{\partial \dot{a}(t)}{\partial \delta_k(t)}\bigg|_{(\bar{k},\bar{a})} & \dfrac{\partial \dot{a}(t)}{\partial A(t)}\bigg|_{(\bar{k},\bar{a})} \end{bmatrix} \qquad (3.13)$$

$$= \begin{bmatrix} 0 & -\bar{k} & \bar{k}^{\varsigma} \\[2mm] -1 & -1 & \dfrac{\rho + \delta_k}{A} \end{bmatrix}$$

Let us start by considering a positive change on the efficiency of the communication process, ΔA. Intuitively, this perturbation will have the following impact over a given steady-state in which the system is supposed to rest: both the quantity of cognitive resources and the expected benefit should see the corresponding values rise, according to the equilibrium results one has found in (3.10). The following analysis will allow to confirm that an increase in parameter A will imply obtaining a steady-state where the endogenous variables will display higher values, it will also allow to quantify such increase, and it allows as well to understand which is the trajectory followed by the variables from the first to the second equilibrium or steady-state point.

The first impact of the perturbation occurs only over the expected benefit variable. As referred before, the agent has no direct possibility of controlling the accumulation of cognitive resources, since this accumulation depends simply on the rule given by (3.3); nevertheless, the agent controls the resources that are channelled to the evaluation and processing of data and, thus, she has control over the expected benefit or reward. Therefore, in a first moment, the perturbation implies an adjustment of the agent's behavior in the direction of diverting resources into the evaluation of choices and decision making. The short-run impact of the perturbation over the control variable is quantified in the following way:

$$\Delta \overline{a}_0 = \Delta \overline{a}_\infty - \frac{p_{21}}{p_{11}} . \Delta \overline{k}_\infty \tag{3.14}$$

In (3.14), $\Delta \overline{a}_0$ represents the immediate effect of a change in the communication efficiency over the expected benefit; $\Delta \overline{a}_\infty$ corresponds to the long-run effect over the expected benefit, i.e., to the difference between the equilibrium value of $a(t)$ after the perturbation and the value of this variable previously to the change on the efficiency of the communication process; $\Delta \overline{k}_\infty$ will correspond to the long-run change of the considered perturbation over the state variable; ratio $\frac{p_{21}}{p_{11}}$ corresponds, as before, to the slope of the stable trajectory.

The immediate impact of the perturbation on A can be computed only if previously one finds the long-run effects of such perturbation. These are straightforward to obtain, by proceeding with the following computation,

$$\begin{bmatrix} \Delta \overline{k}_\infty \\ \Delta \overline{a}_\infty \end{bmatrix} = -J^{-1}.J(X)_A.\Delta A \tag{3.15}$$

In (3.15), J^{-1} will be the inverse matrix of (3.11) and $J(X)_A$ corresponds to the vector of (3.13) relating parameter A. The calculus of the inverse matrix of J yields

$$J^{-1} = \frac{1}{Det(J)} . Adj(J)^T = \begin{bmatrix} 0 & -\frac{1}{1-\zeta} . \frac{\overline{k}}{\rho + \delta_k} \\ -\frac{1}{e^{\overline{a}}} & -\frac{1}{1-\zeta} . \frac{\rho}{\rho + \delta_k} . \frac{\overline{k}}{e^{\overline{a}}} \end{bmatrix} \tag{3.16}$$

Multiplying (3.16) by the vector of exogenous parameters associated to the disturbance in A, we find the long-run changes, the ones that will remain in time after an exogenous change on the level of communication efficiency. The result is,

$$
\begin{bmatrix} \Delta \bar{k}_\infty \\ \Delta \bar{a}_\infty \end{bmatrix} = \begin{bmatrix} \dfrac{1}{1-\zeta} \cdot \dfrac{\bar{k}}{A} \\ \dfrac{1}{A} \cdot \left[1 + \left(\delta_k + \dfrac{\rho}{1-\zeta} \right) \cdot \dfrac{\bar{k}}{e^{\bar{a}}} \right] \end{bmatrix} . \Delta A
\tag{3.17}
$$

The computed multipliers in (3.17) are both positive values, as one would expect. An increase in the communication skills allows for increases in the resources that can be used to evaluate choices and, thus, to stimulate the expected benefit of the decision.

The results in (3.17) reveal the full extent of an evolutionary process from the initial equilibrium to the steady-state arising after the perturbation; this process will correspond to an adjustment over the saddle trajectory that begins after an initial adjustment in the value of the benefit variable, according to expression (3.14). The respective computation implies,

$$
\Delta \bar{a}_0 = \frac{1}{A} \cdot \left[1 + \left(\delta_k + \frac{\lambda_1}{1-\zeta} \right) \frac{\bar{k}}{e^{\bar{a}}} \right] . \Delta A
\tag{3.18}
$$

Perturbation (3.18) will not have an unambiguous sign, since, as previously mentioned, λ_1 is an eigenvalue with a negative sign. Thus, the immediate effect of the increase on the communication efficiency may not correspond to an increase on the expected benefit. This is justified by the fact that in the presence of an increase in the capacity to communicate it can be optimal to divert resources from the decision process that generates the referred benefits, allocating in the short-run additional cognitive resources to interaction through communication. However, this is just a part of the strategy of maximizing the intertemporal flow of expected benefits; in the long-run, as verified, the impact of the larger efficiency over the symbolic interaction implies a positive growth in the available cognitive resources and, thus, a growth in the capacity to evaluate choices and to select the options that best contribute to obtaining the desired benefits.

The graphical illustration of the effect of the perturbation helps perceiving the mechanism that was described above. In figure 3.2 one draws the stable trajectory (3.12) and it is presented the corresponding steady-state point (E). According to (3.18), the shift on the stable trajectory happening as the result of the perturbation can occur to the right or to the left of the initial trajectory; let us assume the most probable case, i.e., the case of a short-run increase in $a(t)$, and thus a shift of the convergence trajectory to the left. The figure will then display the new steady-state point (E'), which will be found above and to the right relatively to the initial equilibrium point; in this long-run scenario, the maximization of expected benefits is translated in a larger benefit but also in a larger endowment of cognitive resources.

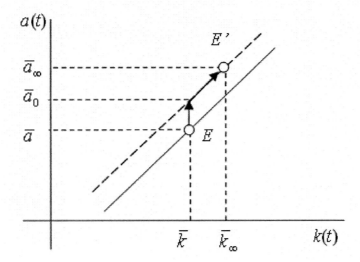

Figure 3.2. Effects of a perturbation on the value of parameter A, over the equilibrium dynamics.

Figure 3.2 clarifies the effect of the perturbation. For a system that rests in a steady-state point E, any event implying a change in the way the use of cognitive resources in the communication process allows to generate additional cognitive resources will imply a change in the position of the equilibrium point. In the specific considered case, an increase in communication efficiency will allow to reach a steady-state representing a larger amount of cognitive resources and a higher expected benefit. The way in which the new steady-state is achieved encloses a particular point: since the agent has the capacity to choose the quantity of cognitive resources she withdraws from communication to proceed with evaluation of benefits, she can immediately adjust the value of the benefits, allowing for an automatic jump towards the new saddle-trajectory, over which both variables will then converge to the steady-state point that the perturbation generates.

Figures 3.3 and 3.4 characterize the dynamic consequences of the positive change in the value of A over the time paths of both variables. These figures represent precisely the time trajectories of the two variables for the case that was characterized in figure 3.2. For variable $k(t)$ there is no initial jump, and consequently the adjustment to the new equilibrium occurs without any discontinuities; for variable $a(t)$ there is an immediate adjustment to the new saddle-path.

A parallel analysis relatively to the one undertaken for parameter A, can be made for the other parameters, ρ and δ_k. In the case of the discount rate, the observation of the steady-state result indicates that a positive perturbation $\Delta\rho$ has a negative impact over the steady-state value of the cognitive resources variable. Relatively to the benefit variable, the long-run effect of this perturbation will not be straightforward to obtain, according with the equilibrium value one has encountered for $a(t)$ in (3.10). As in the case of the perturbation over communication efficiency it will be necessary to distinguish between short-run and long-run effects.

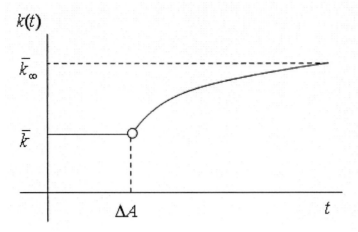

Figure 3.3. Time trajectory of variable $k(t)$, as a function of the positive perturbation in the value of parameter A.

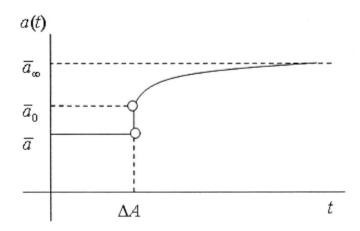

Figure 3.4. Time trajectory of variable $a(t)$, as a function of the positive perturbation in the value of parameter A.

The long-run multipliers are computed in the same way as in (3.15), with the inverse matrix of J given as before by (3.16) and the array of perturbations relating parameter ρ being $J(X)_\rho=[0\ -1]$', with $J(X)$ the matrix in (3.13). The computation leads to the following long-run effects of the perturbation,

$$\begin{bmatrix} \Delta\bar{k}_\infty \\ \Delta\bar{a}_\infty \end{bmatrix} = \begin{bmatrix} -\dfrac{1}{1-\zeta}\cdot\dfrac{\bar{k}}{\rho+\delta_k} \\ -\dfrac{1}{1-\zeta}\cdot\dfrac{\rho}{\rho+\delta_k}\cdot\dfrac{\bar{k}}{e^{\bar{a}}} \end{bmatrix}.\Delta\rho \tag{3.19}$$

The analysis of (3.19) allows quantifying an effect of negative sign over the variables of the model, when there is a positive change on the value of the discount rate of future benefits. We infer that if the agent decides, for any exogenous reason, to increase the value attributed to close in time rewards relatively to far in time rewards this means that in the long-run both the cognitive resources and the expected benefits of the decision will fall. We conclude that impatience in obtaining good results, which implicitly means in the short-run to withdraw a significant amount of resources from communication to allocate them to the decision making process, leads to the achievement of lower long-run results.

There will also be a short-run effect, which can be computed according to expression (3.14). This effect occurs only over the benefit variable. Resorting to the results in (3.19) and recovering the expression of the slope of the stable trajectory, one obtains:

$$\Delta \bar{a}_0 = -\frac{1}{1-\zeta} \cdot \frac{1}{\rho+\delta_k} \cdot \frac{\bar{k}}{e^{\bar{a}}} . \lambda_1 . \Delta \rho \tag{3.20}$$

The initial jump (3.20) corresponds to a positive value (recall that the eigenvalue is negative) and therefore, in the short-run, an increase in the discount rate has a positive effect over the expected benefit: if one attributes a larger value to the current benefit relatively to future ones, optimization will imply that resources will be diverted from communication in the direction of the decision making process, what allows the agent to obtain more significant immediate results but also compromises the long-run benefit.

As in the case of the perturbation over parameter A, also for the perturbation over the discount rate one can undertake a graphical representation of the phase diagram and of the time trajectories. It will be evident an overshooting effect for the expected benefit, rising immediately and progressively falling afterwards. The initial effect forms a new saddle trajectory (to the left of the first, in order to represent an increase in the benefit variable), over which variables will converge towards the new equilibrium in which both variables will exhibit lower values.

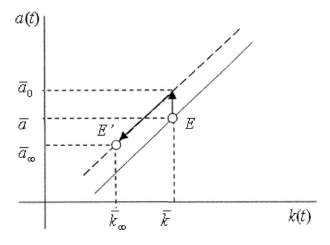

Figure 3.5. Effect of a perturbation in the value of parameter ρ, over the equilibrium dynamics.

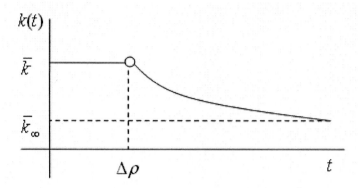

Figure 3.6. Time trajectory of variable $k(t)$, as a function of a positive perturbation in the value of parameter ρ.

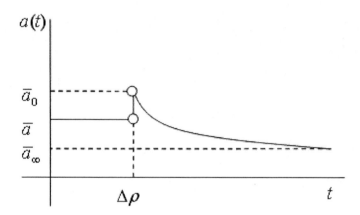

Figure 3.7. Time trajectory of variable $a(t)$, as a function of a positive perturbation in the value of parameter ρ.

A last perturbation to consider relates to the rate at which the cognitive resources depreciate over time. The communication process allows adding cognitive resources; however, the symbolic interaction does not produce a body of knowledge and resources that are perpetuated in time without any loss. Individuals tend to forget part of their conversations and discussions and often set aside some information when new information is acquired; in synthesis, at each time moment there is an evaporation process with a given percentage of the cognitive resources held by the agent being lost. This loss of resources is quantified in the model through parameter δ_k, which we have designated as the rate of depreciation of the cognitive resources.

It will not be difficult to understand the effect of a positive change in the value of the depreciation parameter over the steady-state. This variation should lead, in a long-run perspective, to lower accumulated values of cognitive resources and expected benefit of decisions (recall that we have assumed that the larger benefit is the direct result of more resources associated to the decision making process). The immediate effect of a faster depreciation of resources will be, from the beginning, also negative: lower cognitive resources will prevent the possibility of obtaining an expected benefit as high as before.

In what follows, we quantify the effects of the perturbation $\Delta\delta_k$; since the graphical analysis is similar to previous ones, we will omit it. We begin by computing the long-run multipliers. These are obtained, once again, by considering a formula similar to (3.15), where the relevant array of exogenous variables is now $J(X)_\delta$, which is the array corresponding to the second column of the matrix in (3.13). Undertaking the corresponding computation, we find the following long-run effects,

$$
\begin{bmatrix} \Delta\bar{k}_\infty \\ \Delta\bar{a}_\infty \end{bmatrix} = \begin{bmatrix} -\dfrac{1}{1-\zeta}\cdot\dfrac{\bar{k}}{\rho+\delta_k} \\ -\left[1+\dfrac{1}{1-\zeta}\cdot\dfrac{\rho}{\rho+\delta_k}\right]\cdot\dfrac{\bar{k}}{e^{\bar{a}}} \end{bmatrix}.\Delta\delta_k
\tag{3.21}
$$

In possession of (3.21), we immediately confirm the logical result that a faster loss of cognitive resources will imply a change towards a new steady-state where the amount of accumulated cognitive resources is lower and where the expected benefit is equally lower.

Relatively to the short-run effects, we resort once again to formula (3.14). In this specific case,

$$
\Delta\bar{a}_0 = -\left[1+\dfrac{1}{1-\zeta}\cdot\dfrac{1}{\rho+\delta_k}\cdot\lambda_1\right]\cdot\dfrac{\bar{k}}{e^{\bar{a}}}.\Delta\delta_k
\tag{3.22}
$$

The sign of (3.22) is not easy to determine, but for reasonable values of the stable eigenvalue one should expect the expression to assume a negative value. Anyway, the significant result is the long-run one: a larger capacity to retain communication results contributes in a favorable way to the flow of expected benefits in an intertemporal perspective.

3.3. COMMUNICATIONAL INTERDEPENDENCE

In the model developed along this chapter, an agent attempts to take a decision, relatively to some problem she is faced with, in order to withdraw the largest possible level of benefit or satisfaction. She interacts with other individuals since this is the way to acquire capacities or cognitive resources that feed the decision process. However, this interaction arises in an implicit form. Nothing in the model explains the relevance of the contact with others with the objective of augmenting the cognitive resources. In this section, one intends to offer a small appointment about the way in which the interaction through communication can be presented in a formal way.

The representative agent of the previous section is now an agent i, in an interval that contains an indeterminate number of agents: $i\in[0,N]$. Each agent possesses, in each time moment, a certain quantity of cognitive resources, $k_i(t)$. As in the previously analyzed benchmark model, this quantity of resources is not a fixed value. It grows through the communication process, with some of the resources being deviated to decision making and another part simply disappearing through depreciation. What will distinguish the new formulation of the problem relatively to the previous one will be the shape of the function of accumulation of cognitive resources.

The results of the communication process will not be the outcome only of the individual capabilities but also of interaction and of the establishment of relationships. Thus, it seems logical to assume that the accumulation of cognitive resources is not made just through the use of the own cognitive resources of each agent but according with the participation of all the other agents. The dynamic equation concerning the accumulation of cognitive resources can be rewritten as

$$\dot{k}_i(t) = A.K(t) - e^{a_i(t)} - \delta_k.k_i(t), \ k_i(0) = k_{i0} \text{ given, } i \in [0, N] \tag{3.23}$$

In Equation (3.23), $a_i(t)$ corresponds to the expected benefit of each agent i, the communication efficiency and depreciation parameters are considered identical among agents and variable $K(t)$ will be the communication function through which the cognitive resources are generated. As referred, this will now depend on the actions of all the agents and not only of the isolated agent. The function is defined in the following way:

$$K(t) = \int_0^N k_n(t)^{\zeta_n}.dn \tag{3.24}$$

To maintain the assumption that communication is subject to decreasing returns in what concerns the capacity of generating cognitive resources, we consider that all the parameters ζ_n are positive but bounded below one.

The new version of the model illustrates that the communication process is a process of interaction, and the larger is the contribution of each one in terms of the resources associated to this process, the more the whole of the agents gains in terms of generated resources. To make clear the implications of the new version of the model we assume two agents, i and j.

Considering a same optimization problem as in previous sections, we derive, for the two agents, the dynamic equations relating to the time movement of the variables of expected benefit,

$$\dot{a}_i(t) = \zeta_i.A.k_i(t)^{-(1-\zeta_i)} - (\rho + \delta_k)$$
$$\dot{a}_j(t) = \zeta_j.A.k_j(t)^{-(1-\zeta_j)} - (\rho + \delta_k) \tag{3.25}$$

Besides the same parameters A and δ_k, also the discount rate of future benefits is assumed to be identical across agents. The system of differential equations relatively to which one wants to study the dynamic evolution will be the system composed by the set of Equations (3.23) respecting to agents i and j, and the two Equations in (3.25). To analyze the model we proceed as in the case without interaction: it is necessary to compute the steady-state results, to present the Jacobian matrix corresponding to the linearized version of the model in the vicinity of the steady-state and to find the eigenvalues that allow characterizing the underlying type of dynamics.

The equilibrium results are, in what concerns the accumulated cognitive resources,

$$\bar{k}_i = \left(\frac{\zeta_i.A}{\rho + \delta_k}\right)^{1/(1-\zeta_i)} \; ; \; \bar{k}_j = \left(\frac{\zeta_j.A}{\rho + \delta_k}\right)^{1/(1-\zeta_j)} \tag{3.26}$$

Results (3.26) are distinct from each other only because parameters ζ are not necessarily identical. The steady-state values for the benefit variables are,

$$\bar{a}_i = \ln\left[A.\left(\left(\frac{\zeta_i.A}{\rho + \delta_k}\right)^{\zeta_i/(1-\zeta_i)} + \left(\frac{\zeta_j.A}{\rho + \delta_k}\right)^{\zeta_j/(1-\zeta_j)}\right) - \delta_k.\left(\frac{\zeta_i.A}{\rho + \delta_k}\right)^{1/(1-\zeta_i)}\right] ;$$

$$\bar{a}_j = \ln\left[A.\left(\left(\frac{\zeta_i.A}{\rho + \delta_k}\right)^{\zeta_i/(1-\zeta_i)} + \left(\frac{\zeta_j.A}{\rho + \delta_k}\right)^{\zeta_j/(1-\zeta_j)}\right) - \delta_k.\left(\frac{\zeta_j.A}{\rho + \delta_k}\right)^{1/(1-\zeta_j)}\right] \tag{3.27}$$

Given the steady-state results (3.26) and (3.27) we understand that interaction has a relevant effect over the long-run equilibrium; these results differ from the scenario of a single agent because now the communication result is a function of the explicit interaction process.

Relatively to the Jacobian matrix, this will now be a square matrix of dimension 4, making it unfeasible to proceed with a graphical analysis of the system; hence, the analysis will concentrate in an analytical evaluation.

The matrix to compute will be J_4, matrix in which the various derivatives are evaluated in the vicinity of the steady state,

$$J_4 = \begin{bmatrix} \left.\frac{\partial \dot{k}_i(t)}{\partial k_i(t)}\right|_{Eq.} & \left.\frac{\partial \dot{k}_i(t)}{\partial k_j(t)}\right|_{Eq.} & \left.\frac{\partial \dot{k}_i(t)}{\partial a_i(t)}\right|_{Eq.} & \left.\frac{\partial \dot{k}_i(t)}{\partial a_j(t)}\right|_{Eq.} \\[2ex] \left.\frac{\partial \dot{k}_j(t)}{\partial k_i(t)}\right|_{Eq.} & \left.\frac{\partial \dot{k}_j(t)}{\partial k_j(t)}\right|_{Eq.} & \left.\frac{\partial \dot{k}_j(t)}{\partial a_i(t)}\right|_{Eq.} & \left.\frac{\partial \dot{k}_j(t)}{\partial a_j(t)}\right|_{Eq.} \\[2ex] \left.\frac{\partial \dot{a}_i(t)}{\partial k_i(t)}\right|_{Eq.} & \left.\frac{\partial \dot{a}_i(t)}{\partial k_j(t)}\right|_{Eq.} & \left.\frac{\partial \dot{a}_i(t)}{\partial a_i(t)}\right|_{Eq.} & \left.\frac{\partial \dot{a}_i(t)}{\partial a_j(t)}\right|_{Eq.} \\[2ex] \left.\frac{\partial \dot{a}_j(t)}{\partial k_i(t)}\right|_{Eq.} & \left.\frac{\partial \dot{a}_j(t)}{\partial k_j(t)}\right|_{Eq.} & \left.\frac{\partial \dot{a}_j(t)}{\partial a_i(t)}\right|_{Eq.} & \left.\frac{\partial \dot{a}_j(t)}{\partial a_j(t)}\right|_{Eq.} \end{bmatrix}$$

The corresponding computation allows obtaining (3.28).

$$J_4 = \begin{bmatrix} \rho & \rho+\delta_k & -e^{\overline{a}_i} & 0 \\ \dfrac{\rho+\delta_k}{} & \rho & 0 & -e^{\overline{a}_j} \\ -(1-\zeta_i).\dfrac{\rho+\delta_k}{\overline{k}_i} & 0 & 0 & 0 \\ 0 & -(1-\zeta_j).\dfrac{\rho+\delta_k}{\overline{k}_j} & 0 & 0 \end{bmatrix} \qquad (3.28)$$

In the model with communication interaction, the type of dynamics can, once more, be characterized through the computation of eigenvalues. The matrix has a dimension higher than two, what means that it is necessary to compute more than the trace and the determinant in order to obtain the signs of the eigenvalues of the matrix. The trace is $Tr(J_4)=2.\rho$ and the determinant comes $Det(J_4)=(1-\zeta_i).(1-\zeta_j).\dfrac{\rho+\delta_k}{\overline{k}_i.\overline{k}_j}.e^{\overline{a}_i}.e^{\overline{a}_j}$. From the previous values, one withdraws a first conclusion about possible dynamic outcomes: since the sum of all the eigenvalues (the trace of the matrix) is a positive value and the product of the four eigenvalues (the determinant of the matrix) is also a positive value, then two of the eigenvalues will be positive and the other two negative, what implies a saddle-path equilibrium, or alternatively the eigenvalues are all positive and the equilibrium will be unstable.

To rigorously present the signs of the eigenvalues one must compute the sums of the principle minors of order 2, $M(2)$, and of order 3, $M(3)$. In reality, finding solely the value $M(2)=\rho^2-(\rho+\delta_k)^2-(1-\zeta_i).\dfrac{\rho+\delta_k}{\overline{k}_i}.e^{\overline{a}_i}-(1-\zeta_j).\dfrac{\rho+\delta_k}{\overline{k}_j}.e^{\overline{a}_j}$, and noticing that this is negative, given the rule $M(2)=\displaystyle\sum_{\substack{i=1 \\ j=1}}^{4}\lambda_i.\lambda_j$, then negative eigenvalues will have to exist.

Putting together this and the previous information, one confirms that two of the eigenvalues are negative values while the other two are positive, and therefore a saddle-path equilibrium exists. With interaction, and considering two agents, we have doubled the dimension of the system; the saddle and anti-saddle trajectories (stable and unstable trajectories, respectively) become two-dimensional areas instead of straight lines.

The computation of the analytical expression of the stable trajectory is possible but the eigenvectors will correspond in this case to combinations of parameters that are too heavy and thus their presentation does not make much sense. However, intuitively one understands that the variables cognitive resources and expected benefit should evolve, as before, in the same direction as they converge to the steady-state: communication will be a process through which symbolic interaction among agents allows, for all the involved agents, to accumulate cognitive resources that help in making well informed and well thought decisions in order to obtain the highest possible level of benefit or utility.

The extension of the communication and cognition model undertaken in this section has characterized the way in which communication through interaction adds value to the resources that the individuals have at their disposal to make educated choices. Therefore, more than having a concern in presenting specific analytical results, it is important the interpretation one makes of a function like (3.24); The general notion is that the larger is the amount of individuals participating in the exchange of ideas and the larger is the amount of cognitive resources that they make available to the interaction process, the more all the players will benefit from such fact.

3.4. COMMUNICATIONAL EFFICIENCY

Another possible extension of the model consists in transforming into an endogenous variable the communicational efficiency parameter, A. Recovering the original model of sections 3.1 and 3.2, assume that the dynamics of efficiency in the communication process is a function of the already accumulated efficiency, such that we consider differential Equation (3.29).

$$\dot{A}(t) = g.A(t)^{\xi} - \delta_A.A(t) \quad A(0)=A_0 \text{ given} \tag{3.29}$$

In (3.29), g is a positive parameter, δ_A respects to a rate of efficiency loss in communication and $\xi>0$ represents the type of returns associated to the growth of efficiency. For this last parameter, a value below one implies decreasing returns and therefore a tendency for the efficiency in communication to stop growing in the long-run; constant returns, translated in condition $\xi=1$, imply an efficiency that grows forever at a constant rate, and increasing returns, $\xi>1$, indicate a tendency of ever increasing growth. We will address the two most probable situations, the ones concerning decreasing returns and constant returns.

In the presence of decreasing returns, Equation (3.29) can be included in the problem of optimization of the communication result; in this new problem, there will be an additional

steady-state result, which is $\overline{A} = \left(\dfrac{g}{\delta_A} \right)^{1/(1-\xi)}$. This result will add to (3.10). The Jacobian

matrix will now have dimension 3; the matrix in (3.11) gives place to

$$J_3 = \begin{bmatrix} \rho & -e^{\overline{a}} & \overline{k}^{\zeta} \\ -(1-\zeta).\dfrac{\rho+\delta_k}{\overline{k}} & 0 & \dfrac{\rho+\delta_k}{A} \\ 0 & 0 & -(1-\xi).\delta_A \end{bmatrix} \tag{3.30}$$

The eigenvalues of (3.30) are λ_1 and λ_2, such that $\lambda_1+\lambda_2=\rho$, $\lambda_1.\lambda_2=-(1-\zeta).\dfrac{\rho+\delta_k}{\overline{k}}.e^{\overline{a}}$,

and $\lambda_3=-(1-\xi).\delta_A$. Thus, we have introduced an additional dimension of stability into the model. The saddle-trajectory is no longer a line but a two-dimensional area; the unstable dimension continues to correspond to a one-dimensional line, since we find a unique positive eigenvalue.

Again, the determination of the stable trajectory becomes cumbersome in terms of computation, but it has to give place to an expression of the type $a(t) - \bar{a} = x_1 \cdot [k(t) - \bar{k}] + x_2 \cdot [A(t) - \bar{A}]$, where x_1 and x_2 are positive values that represent a joint evolution of equal sign between each of the state variables $k(t)$ and $A(t)$ and the variable that is subject to optimization, $a(t)$, as the system converges to the steady-state. We conclude that if efficiency grows but at a progressively lower rate, the final result will not differ significantly from the one in the original version, existing a steady-state point for which convergence occurs as long as the system is located over the stable trajectory.

In the case in which communicational efficiency grows at a constant rate ($\xi=1$), to solve the model we cannot use a same approach as before. Now, we no longer have a steady-state with constant values of variables. Since, according to (3.10), the steady-state values of the cognitive resources and of the expected benefit depend positively on A, then they will also grow at a positive rate (as long as $g > \delta_A$).

Noticing that $\dfrac{\dot{A}(t)}{A(t)} = g - \delta_A$, the following are the growth rates in the steady-state:

$$\frac{\dot{k}}{k} = \frac{1}{1-\zeta} \cdot \frac{\dot{A}}{A} \quad \text{and} \quad \frac{\dot{a}}{a} = \frac{1}{1-\zeta} \cdot \frac{1}{\bar{a}} \cdot \frac{\dot{A}}{A}.$$ The systematic growth of the communicational

efficiency means that the dynamic process is extended beyond the transitional phase into the steady-state. In this, the capacity to communicate continues to grow and with it also grows the stock of cognitive resources and the expected benefit of decisions. Notice as well that in the long-run scenario the positive change in the communicational efficiency has a multiplier effect over the variation on the cognitive resources; since $1/(1-\zeta)>1$, then the growth of the efficiency in communication implies an even stronger growth of the cognitive capabilities that the agent develops given the problem at hand.

In this chapter, the notion of communication as a dynamic process was characterized having in consideration the intertemporal evolution of the benefit that can be withdrawn from the decision making process. In chapter 2 we have mentioned that communication weights a learning factor and an entropy factor in order to choose between options, given the expected benefit of each action. Such analysis was important to understand the effects of communication over choices; however, the analysis was silent about the way in which the systematic participation in processes of symbolic interaction can help in achieving optimal results.

By adopting a modelling structure where the intertemporal flow of expected benefits from a given sequence of actions is maximized, it became clear that the agent has options and controls her own actions. The developed simple model has allowed to connect communication with options regarding the allocation of resources and with the achievement of expected results.

To the agent was given the freedom to act with the intent of choosing between being involved in the communication process, where she collects information, shares experiences and gains beliefs, and being concentrated in the processing of information and evaluation of alternatives in order to take the best possible decisions. Through the first activity, the agent gathers important elements to the decision making, through the second she decides. By considering that the cognitive resources are rival resources, the agent has to decide at each time moment where to allocate resources: communication or decision making.

The conceived problem encloses a notion of continuity in time. The issue at hand is never static; the decision process is continuous and knowing that this is fed by the resources that communication produces, one needs to equate how the communication resources will be used to maximize the expected benefit of a decision given all the future time moments (which are discounted to the present).

By solving the model, we have achieved a dynamic result where the steady-state locus is accomplished only if the stable trajectory is followed. Once over the equilibrium trajectory, the variables will converge following a pattern where the accumulated quantity of cognitive resources grows, i.e., where the communication process is intensified and where the decision making process will involve a higher quality, allowing for a higher expected benefit. In the steady-state, the expected benefit will be constant, given that the distribution of resources between communication effort and evaluation of alternatives will reach equilibrium.

Some parameters have assumed a relevant role and they were addressed as important sources of perturbation over the steady-state. In particular, the efficiency with which one communicates, which is translated in a given capacity to accumulate cognitive resources when some quantity of cognitive resources is employed in the communication process, has assumed a relevant role. Obviously, the higher is the efficiency with which one communicates, and therefore the larger is the capacity of choice one acquires through the interaction with others, the better will be the expectations in terms of the results to obtain.

The model has also addressed the concern that communication is not an isolated act. When we communicate, we interact with others and the joint effort made by the several players allows to stimulate the accumulation of cognitive resources of each of the players: there is a spillover effect. We have confirmed, through the developed analytical structure, that the communication result and consequent impact over the processes of optimal decision, is directly dependent on the number of individuals involved in the interaction, and above all on the effort that each one employs in order to generate additional resources that are indispensable to the decision.

3.5. APPLICATIONS

Application 1

Assume the array of parameters $[A \; \zeta \; \delta_k \; \rho]=[1 \; 0.75 \; 0.01 \; 0.02]$. For the initial model of sections 3.1 and 3.2 and for the specific assumed values,

a) Explain the way in which the interaction through communication produces cognitive resources;
b) Find the equilibrium values of the variables 'cognitive resources' and 'expected benefit';
c) Represent graphically the stable trajectory along which the variables converge to the steady-state;

d) Assume a positive increase on the communication capabilities of the agent, such that a new parameter $A'=2$ characterizes the efficiency of the communication process. Quantify the short and long-run effects that arise as a consequence of the perturbation.

A. Interaction through Communication Produces Cognitive Resources

The scenario that was considered in this chapter intends to characterize the way in which communication produces a direct result or product, which was designated by 'cognitive resources'. The final goal of the interaction process is not, however, to obtain and accumulate resources; the resources have a specific purpose which is related with their use in the process of decision making. One assumes that the stronger is the effort that the agent employs in the decision the larger will be the utility or benefit that she will withdraw from the choices that are made.

This framework is generic and abstract. When we refer to cognitive resources, to the expected result of the decision or to the way in which communication produces resources, no situation or sequence of situations is specifically considered, and therefore multiple types of interaction and choice processes may be assumed.

The analytical structure has, nevertheless, two points at its favour: on one hand, it describes a dynamic process; the agent does not decide only by looking at the present moment, on the contrary she manages the available resources in order to attain an optimal allocation of resources between communication and decision making over time. More than having a concern with the immediate result, the agent chooses trajectories of allocation of cognitive resources that allow for the intertemporal maximization of the results that in terms of choice the communication will allow for. On the other hand, the model describes precisely an optimal behavior oriented to the best possible allocation of resources; the agent will have to make a choice today given some future horizon, and by knowing the peculiarities of the considered process she can do it in order to maximize expected outcomes.

For the specific analytical structure one has considered, the way in which the employment of cognitive resources in the communication process generates additional resources implies the consideration of a production function. The cognitive resources available at each time moment for the symbolic interaction with others, $k(t)$, will be subject to a stimulus through which they will be transformed into additional resources; such stimulus emerges from interaction through communication. Function (3.1) represents precisely this production function: resorting to communication, the agent uses a quantity of cognitive resources $k(t)$ in order to obtain an additional quantity of cognitive resources, $y(t)$.

The way in which communication generates added value depends on two parameters, the efficiency in communication, A, and a parameter that reflects the presence of decreasing marginal returns on the accumulation of resources, ζ. This second parameter furnishes a clue about the possibility of communication continuing to be able to add value when the knowledge over a given subject is already a relatively high value; thus, the higher is the value of this parameter, the less important will be the decreasing returns and therefore communication continues to have a relevant role on the accumulation of resources, even when these are already accumulated in a large quantity.

In the case of the exercise, $\zeta=0.75$, a value that reveals that the decreasing returns of communication are not excessively accentuated. Parameter A translates the absolute level of communication efficiency; the higher is the value of this parameter, the more cognitive resources are produced from the same accumulated stock of resources.

For the specific situation of this exercise, we can write the production function of the cognitive resources as $y(t) = k(t)^{0.75}$; this function characterizes the way in which communication generates new resources from previously accumulated resources.

B. Find the Equilibrium Values of the Variables 'Cognitive Resources' and 'Expected Benefit'

The optimal control problem was solved, in its generic form, throughout section 3.2. In the present specific case one has:

$$Max \int_0^{+\infty} a(t).e^{-0.02.t} .dt$$

subject to $\dot{k}(t) = k(t)^{0.75} - e^{a(t)} - 0.01.k(t)$, $k(0) = k_0$ given

By solving the model, one has arrived to the differential Equation (3.9), which reveals the time motion of the expected benefit variable. For the considered parameter values, $\dot{a}(t) = 0.75.k(t)^{-0.25} - 0.03$. The steady-state values of the variables of the model can be determined by solving system $[\dot{k}(t), \dot{a}(t)] = (0,0)$. In its generic form, the corresponding equilibrium result was presented in (3.10). For the specific case in appreciation one computes the following values: $\bar{k} = 390,625$; $\bar{a} = 9.369$.

C. Represent the Stable Trajectory

The graphical representation of the stable trajectory can be undertaken through the construction of a phase diagram similar to the one in figure 3.1. In this, the stable trajectory presents itself with a positive slope, with this a larger slope than the one of isocline $\dot{k}(t) = 0$, which, in this case, is $\dfrac{\rho}{e^{\bar{a}}} = 1.7 \times 10^{-6}$.

For a more rigorous graphical presentation of the stable trajectory, one can compute the corresponding analytical expression. Once again, knowing the generic expression, (3.12), we can simply replace in it the specific parameter values of the exercise. We also need to compute the concrete value of the negative eigenvalue of the Jacobian matrix. From Jacobian matrix (3.11) one withdraws the trace and the determinant expressions, which for the example in consideration are $Tr(J)=0.02$ and $Det(J)=-0.225 \times 10^{-3}$. These values allow presenting the characteristic equation $\lambda^2 - 0.02.\lambda - 0.225 \times 10^{-3} = 0$. The solutions of this equation are the eigenvalues $\lambda_1 = -8.028 \times 10^{-3}$ and $\lambda_2 = 2.803 \times 10^{-2}$.

We can now resort to the negative eigenvalue in order to display the expression of the saddle-trajectory. Replacing the several values in (3.12), one obtains: $a(t) = 8.435 + 2.392 \times 10^{-6}.k(t)$. The stable trajectory is a straight line relatively close to the horizontal position (its slope is a low value), but one confirms that this slope is larger than the one of the mentioned isocline line. The low inclination of the saddle-trajectory implies that in the period of adjustment or transition towards the steady-state, large variations in the quantity of cognitive resources are needed in order to have a somehow significant impact over the expected benefit variable.

The following figure draws the stable trajectory, which obviously passes through the computed steady-state point.

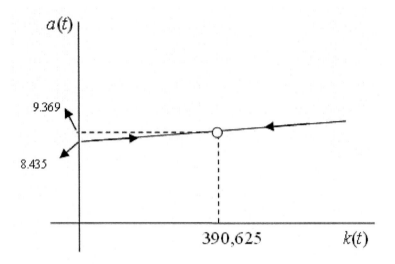

D. Assume a Positive Increase on the Communication Capabilities of the Agent

The increase in the communicational efficiency disturbs the steady-state that at a given point in time may characterize the problem of communication and decision of an agent. In the case in appreciation the perturbation will be $\Delta A=1$.

The effects of this kind of perturbation were characterized in section 3.2. Through (3.13) one has determined a perturbation array that has allowed to calculate the short and long-run impact of the variation on the communicational capacity parameter. These effects are presented in their generic form in (3.18) and in (3.17), respectively. Figure 3.2 furnishes a general overview of the impact of a variation on A. The system initially rests over an equilibrium point; by modifying the value of the parameter, one is provoking an immediate jump towards the new saddle-trajectory that will locate to the left of the first; this jump will correspond to an instantaneous change on the value of the expected benefit of the decision. This effect is the result of an immediate reaction of the agent, which will reallocate her cognitive resources between the two activities (communicate and decide) in order for the model to continue to generate optimal decisions; once the new stable trajectory is attained, the variables will converge, over it, to the new steady-state point that is produced by the perturbation.

As figure 3.2 makes clear, and as under an intuitive point of view one should expect, larger efficiency in communication implies a faster accumulation of cognitive resources and, therefore, more accumulated cognitive resources in the long-run and an increased availability to use them to take decisions, what implies also a larger value of the expected benefit variable.

To arrive to the values describing the effects of the perturbation, one can resort directly to (3.17) and (3.18). The long-run impact of the perturbation is given by,

$$\begin{bmatrix} \Delta \bar{k}_\infty \\ \Delta \bar{a}_\infty \end{bmatrix} = \begin{bmatrix} 1,562,500 \\ 2.08 \end{bmatrix}.$$

These results correspond to the long-run change triggered by the increase in the communicational efficiency. The new equilibrium, that will remain, will be $\bar{k} + \Delta \bar{k}_\infty = 1,953,125$; $\bar{a} + \Delta \bar{a}_\infty = 11.449$. To achieve this equilibrium a new saddle-trajectory is followed, to which one jumps immediately in the moment of the perturbation; the extent of the jump is given by the change in the value of variable $a(t)$. The initial jump (3.18) will be, in the present case, $\Delta \bar{a}_0 = 0.735$. Thus, variable $a(t)$ leaves the equilibrium value $\bar{a} = 9.369$ to immediately assume value $\bar{a} + \Delta \bar{a}_0 = 10.104$. From this point forward there is a joint convergence movement of this value and of value $k(t)$ towards the steady-state.

The following figure summarizes the path followed by the variables as the result of the assumed perturbation. In this case, by doubling the communicational efficiency, there will be a large change in the amount of cognitive resources and a not so pronounced positive variation in the value of the expected benefit.

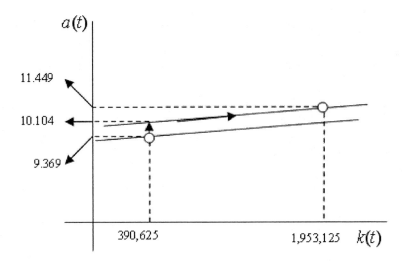

Application 2

Consider the communicational interdependence model of section 3.3.

a) For a non specified number of agents, present the Jacobian matrix concerning the linearized system one obtains after solving the dynamic optimization problem;

b)   Assuming $N=2$ and the vector of parameters $[A\ \zeta_i\ \zeta_j\ \delta_k\ \rho]=[0.5\ 0.6\ 0.5\ 0.01\ 0.02]$, determine the analytical expression of the saddle-trajectory.

A. Present the Jacobian Matrix

In section 3.3, the optimization scenario in presence of interdependence through communication was presented for $N>1$ agents, but the detailed analysis was undertaken for the particular case $N=2$. One has observed that it continues to exist a saddle-path equilibrium, since although the interdependency makes the communication results depend on the resources applied by others in the interaction process, this fact does not change the qualitative structure of the model: by doubling the dimension of the system under analysis, one also doubles the dimension of both the stable and the unstable trajectories.

For N agents, the nature of the model is maintained as well, and the corresponding stable trajectory will have dimension N. This dimension corresponds to the number of eigenvalues of negative sign of the Jacobian matrix that the exercise asks to determine. This matrix will have a dimension $2.N$ and we will designate it by $J_{2.n}$

The system one intends to linearize is composed by $2.N$ equations, which are:

$$\dot{k}_i(t) = A.\int_0^N k_n(t)^{\zeta_n.dn} - e^{a_i(t)} - \delta_k.k_i(t),\ k_i(0) = k_{i0}\text{ given, }i \in [0,N]$$

$$\dot{a}_i(t) = \zeta_i.A.k_i(t)^{-(1-\zeta_i)} - (\rho + \delta_k),\ i \in [0,N]$$

Thus, the required Jacobian matrix is simply the following generalization of (3.28),

$$J_{2.N} = \begin{bmatrix} \rho & \rho+\delta_k & \cdots & \rho+\delta_k & -e^{\bar{a}_1} & 0 & \cdots & 0 \\ \rho+\delta_k & \rho & \cdots & \rho+\delta_k & 0 & -e^{\bar{a}_2} & \cdots & 0 \\ \vdots & \vdots & \ddots & \vdots & \vdots & \vdots & \ddots & \vdots \\ \rho+\delta_k & \rho+\delta_k & \cdots & \rho & 0 & 0 & \cdots & -e^{\bar{a}_N} \\ \hline j_1 & 0 & \cdots & 0 & 0 & 0 & \cdots & 0 \\ 0 & j_2 & \cdots & 0 & 0 & 0 & \cdots & 0 \\ \vdots & \vdots & \ddots & \vdots & \vdots & \vdots & \ddots & \vdots \\ 0 & 0 & \cdots & j_N & 0 & 0 & \cdots & 0 \end{bmatrix}$$

with $j_i = -(1-\zeta_i).\dfrac{\rho+\delta_k}{\bar{k}_i}$, $i=1,...,N$.

As one observes, the computed matrix does not differ from (3.28), except on its dimension.

B. Determine the Analytical Expression of the Saddle-Trajectory

The determination of the expression of the stable trajectory requires the presentation of the Jacobian matrix of the model and the computation of eigenvalues and eigenvectors. A first step consists in the determination of the equilibrium values of the cognitive resources and of the expected benefit, for each one of the agents, i and j.

These equilibrium values are given by (3.26) and (3.27), and therefore we just need to proceed with the corresponding replacement of the parameters by the corresponding values given on the exercise. The following array of steady-state values is found:

$$\begin{bmatrix} \bar{k}_i \\ \bar{k}_j \\ \bar{a}_i \\ \bar{a}_j \end{bmatrix} = \begin{bmatrix} 316.228 \\ 69.444 \\ 2.822 \\ 2.959 \end{bmatrix}$$

These steady-state values display differences among agents simply because one has assumed different parameters reflecting the extent of the decreasing returns on the accumulation of cognitive resources. Thus, the agent for whom the decreasing returns are more accentuated (agent i) achieves, in the long-run, a larger quantity of resources. Relatively to the expected benefit, we remind that in this interaction scenario communication uses resources of both agents to generate additional resources; the one that accumulates less resources (j), will be the one to obtain a larger long-run expected benefit, since she will make use of the resources from others in order to obtain resources that will be channelled to the decision making process.

In possession of the equilibrium values, one can present the linearized system by accounting for the Jacobian matrix in (3.28). In this particular case,

$$\begin{bmatrix} \dot{k}_i(t) \\ \dot{k}_j(t) \\ \dot{a}_i(t) \\ \dot{a}_j(t) \end{bmatrix} = \begin{bmatrix} 0.02 & 0.03 & -16.816 & 0 \\ 0.03 & 0.02 & 0 & -19.284 \\ -3.795\times10^{-5} & 0 & 0 & 0 \\ 0 & -0.216\times10^{-3} & 0 & 0 \end{bmatrix} \begin{bmatrix} k_i(t)-\bar{k}_i \\ k_j(t)-\bar{k}_j \\ a_i(t)-\bar{a}_i \\ a_j(t)-\bar{a}_j \end{bmatrix}$$

The presented Jacobian matrix has positive trace and determinant values, as one had already noticed in the generic case: $Tr(J)=0.04$ and $Det(J)=2.658\times10^{-6}$. The eigenvalues, two negative and two positive, are $\lambda_1=-6.102\times10^{-2}$, $\lambda_2=-1.597\times10^{-2}$, $\lambda_3=3.217\times10^{-2}$ and $\lambda_4=8,482\times10^{-2}$. The determination of the expression of the stable trajectory implies the computation of the eigenvectors associated with the negative eigenvalues; the following are two admissible eigenvectors,

-Eigenvector associated with λ_1: $P_1 = \begin{bmatrix} -0.391 \\ 0.920 \\ -2.433\times10^{-4} \\ 3.258\times10^{-3} \end{bmatrix}$;

-Eigenvector associated with λ_2: $P_2 = \begin{bmatrix} -0.991 \\ -2.356 \times 10^{-3} \\ -2.356 \times 10^{-3} \\ -1.789 \times 10^{-3} \end{bmatrix}$.

Considering a matrix $P=[P_1 \ P_2]$, the slope of the saddle-trajectory corresponds to the multiplication of the sub-matrix of P relating the control variables (the two last lines of the matrix), by the inverse of the sub-matrix of P relating the two state variables (the inverse matrix of the matrix formed by the two first lines). The following matrix, found after the described computation procedure, corresponds to the slope of the stable trajectory,

$D = \begin{bmatrix} 2.283 \times 10^{-3} & 7.061 \times 10^{-4} \\ 1.261 \times 10^{-3} & 4.076 \times 10^{-3} \end{bmatrix}$. This slope is not a unique value because the stable

trajectory is not one-dimensional. The stable trajectory corresponds to the following expression:

$$\begin{bmatrix} a_i(t) - \bar{a}_i \\ a_j(t) - \bar{a}_j \end{bmatrix} = D.\begin{bmatrix} k_i(t) - \bar{k}_i \\ k_j(t) - \bar{k}_j \end{bmatrix}.$$

Recovering the equilibrium values, one will have, finally,

$$a_i(t) = 2.051 + 2.283 \times 10^{-3}.k_i(t) + 7.061 \times 10^{-4}.k_j(t)$$
$$a_j(t) = 2.277 + 1.261 \times 10^{-3}.k_i(t) + 4.076 \times 10^{-3}.k_j(t)$$

The stable trajectory is two-dimensional and reveals that the expected benefit of both agents will vary, in the transition to the steady-state, as a result of the change in the cognitive resources of the two agents. We confirm a positive sign relation: in a system where cognitive resources grow through interaction and resource sharing, additional communication and consequently a growing stock of cognitive resources, implies an increase on the expected benefit for each one of the agents.

Application 3

Assuming that communicational efficiency grows following the rule $\dot{A}(t) = 0.1.A(t)^{0.1} - 0.02.A(t)$,

a) Compute the equilibrium value of the efficiency variable;
b) For the remaining values of parameters: $\zeta=0.25$; $\delta_k=0.05$ and $\rho=0.05$, find the stable trajectory in this case and explain its meaning.

A. Compute the Equilibrium Value of the Efficiency Variable

The required steady-state value is simply the result of solving $\dot{A}(t) = 0$, that is,

$$\overline{A} = (0.1 / 0.02)^{1/(1-0.1)} = 5.979.$$

B. Find the Stable Trajectory and Explain its Meaning

The model with endogenous communicational efficiency was approached in section 3.4, where one has computed Jacobian matrix (3.30). For the parameter values of this exercise, the Jacobian matrix will be:

$$J_3 = \begin{bmatrix} 0.05 & -12.884 & 2.463 \\ -2.037 \times 10^{-3} & 0 & 1.673 \times 10^{-2} \\ 0 & 0 & -0.018 \end{bmatrix},$$

where, for $\overline{A} = 5.979$, we have the equilibrium values $\overline{k} = 36.821$ and $\overline{a} = 2.556$.

In the same way as in the previous application, the determination of the equilibrium trajectory requires the computation of eigenvalues and eigenvectors. The found eigenvalues are: $\lambda_1 = -0.488$; $\lambda_2 = -0.018$ and $\lambda_3 = 0.538$. The two first eigenvalues are negative, and to these there will correspond the eigenvectors:

-Eigenvector associated to λ_1: $P_1 = \begin{bmatrix} -5.999 \\ -5.932 \times 10^{-2} \\ 1 \end{bmatrix}$;

-Eigenvector associated to λ_2: $P_2 = \begin{bmatrix} 189.47 \\ 1 \\ 0 \end{bmatrix}$.

To obtain the slope of the stable trajectory we multiply the vector formed by the last elements of each eigenvector by the inverse of the square matrix of order two formed by the two first elements of each eigenvector.

As a result, the stable trajectory is:

$$a(t) - \overline{a} = \begin{bmatrix} 1 & 0 \end{bmatrix} \begin{bmatrix} -5.999 & 189.47 \\ -5.932 \times 10^{-2} & 1 \end{bmatrix}^{-1} \begin{bmatrix} k(t) - \overline{k} \\ A(t) - \overline{A} \end{bmatrix}.$$

Simplifying,

$$a(t) - \overline{a} = 0.191.\left[k(t) - \overline{k}\right] - 36.156.\left[A(t) - \overline{A}\right] \Rightarrow$$

$$a(t) = 211.7 + 0.191.k(t) - 36.156.A(t)$$

The computed stable trajectory indicates how the variables in the model relate in the convergence to the steady-state. For the specific assumed values, an initial state in which $k(0) < \overline{k}$ and $A(0) < \overline{A}$ will imply a convergence process towards the equilibrium in which an increase on the amount of cognitive resources contributes to a larger expected benefit and where the higher standards of communicational efficiency diverts resources from the decision making to the communication process, implying a decrease in the benefit that comes from the optimal evaluation of resource allocation.

Chapter 4

CORPORATE COMMUNICATION

An organization is a complex net of relations; it puts together in the same space a group of individuals that interact in order to pursue a previously specified goal. This is in fact an extremely vague notion; however, the ambiguity of the definition reflects something very important, namely the heterogeneity of organizations that will exist in an organized society: private firms, non profit organizations, sports associations, political parties, institutions designed to manage public policies and common goods, among many other types of organized groups that serve a given type of interests.

Inside each organization there are individuals that have their own goals, ambitions and desires, which can be compatible with the overall role that the organization is supposed to play, or on the contrary can collide with such role. Inside the organizations, the individuals take positions and act with the purpose of acquiring a larger recognition from their pairs and hierarchical superiors and in order to create their own identity in the context of the broader organizational identity.

As chapter 1 has emphasized, interpersonal relationships inside organizations assume specific profiles. The relation that is established between a hierarchical superior and her subordinate will be different from the one that is developed between colleagues that execute a same task. The diversity of behavior and interactions must be acknowledged and managed in order to achieve the best interest of the organization. It is a responsibility of the ones occupying the highest ranks in the organization to acquire a global view on the general objectives of the organization and to be able to stimulate the other players of the organization in order to understand the relevance of their job in order to attain the common goal.

Organizational communication will have, in this perspective, a central purpose: it will be through the creation of an effective communication system, a system able to develop a common language understood and apprehend by all, that will be possible to make each one of the members of the organization to work under a common objective, which is to fulfil the mission the organization is oriented for.

In an organization, communication has a well defined goal: the creation of a specific language or code that is understood by its members and that should simplify processes and contribute to efficiency by forming a body of tacit knowledge that will be specific to the organization. Katz and Kahn (1966) and Arrow (1974) go even further, by suggesting that the existence of organizations has as its main purpose to save in terms of the costs associated with information processing. If this saving is not possible or if it is understood as not so important, individuals could work in isolation without the need of an institutional framing. If institutions exist it is because there is an advantage on pursuing collective tasks, which partially involve the creation of communication routines, that generate a particular implicit language and that generally promote higher efficiency and effectiveness standards in the way the organization works and relating the results it can achieve.

We have referred that organizations exist because they have a certain mission to fulfil and because the formation of groups of individuals to which a common language can be passed on is the most reasonable form of fulfilling such mission. The missions of the organizations are so varied as the types of organizations that exist; however, throughout the chapter, we will concentrate on a specific type of organization: the firm; to this organization we can associate a primary goal that offers no ambiguity, i.e., the maximization of profits. Profits are defined as the difference between revenues or income of the developed activity and the associated costs of production.

Therefore, throughout the chapter one discusses the relevance of the communication in firms, to which we will often associate the designation of corporate communication. Being the firm a group of individuals in permanent contact and interaction, communication arises naturally; thus, we will not be concerned with interpersonal symbolic interaction that occurs in firms but also occurs on any other social setting. Instead, we will associate the notion of corporate communication to the oriented effort in creating, through a rational and planned process of sharing of information and beliefs, a common language capable of minimizing conflict behaviors and actions and capable of maximizing attitudes and behaviors directed to achieve the common goal of profit maximization.

As it is obvious, communication oriented at pursuing the specified goals brings advantages to firms, but this will not occur without incurring in costs. Arrow (1985) and Radner (1993) stress the costs that corporate communication involves; any organizational structure needs to update information constantly and also needs to improve communication channels, and these activities have costs, meaning that they will be undertaken only if the expected benefits exceed such costs.

Various authors, as Prescott and Visscher (1980) and Chowhdry and Garmaise (2003), develop the concept of organizational capital. Starting from the simple idea that a firm is a set of assets, these can be distinguished in several categories: physical capital, which includes machines, equipments and buildings; human capital, which is related to the abilities of the individuals that work in the firm regarding their productivity; and organizational capital, which can be defined as the set of intangible assets that allow for a larger efficiency of the tangible assets.

The notion of organizational capital that we will adopt will be somehow a little bit narrower than the one presented in the previous paragraph, which is the one adopted by Kreps (1990) and Hermalin (2001). From this definition we remove some assets that although being intangible are directly attached to the quality of the physical capital and of the human capital and, for this reason, are under the direct control of the firm's shareholders: we are referring to patents, brands and intellectual property in general. Taking these items out, it remains on the notion of organizational capital what we can designate by the language of the firm.

The organizational capital, understood as the internal language of the firm, corresponds to the degree in which the workers in an organization are able to understand each other and to the effectiveness with which communication is translated into concrete actions. The concept of internal language of the firm was developed by Crémer (1993), De Marzo, Vayanos and

Zwiebel (2003) and Garicano (2000), and according to these authors, the referred notion relates essentially to the informal routines of the work, to the specific vocabulary (not only verbal) that is developed and the implicit set of past experiences. Note, particularly, the relevance of past experiences as an element of the organizational capital; a firm that has just been created and possessing a same amount of physical capital and human capital relatively to other firm that is already installed in the market for some time, will certainly generate less value, what will be due to the lower level of organizational capital that has been accumulated. The organizational capital is related to a certain compromise that is generated between the members of an organization, and this can be achieved through a process of communication that is efficient, perpetuated in time and goal oriented.

From the previous idea one must retain the notion that the organizational capital does not differ totally from the other forms of capital, since it also has to be accumulated through a process of investment rationally oriented towards that end. If the installed firm has more organizational capital than a firm that is now starting its activity is because the first had time in the past to undertake the investment capable of straightening the internal language. As for other forms of capital, the accumulation of organizational capital is essential to guarantee increased production results.

An important difference between organizational capital and the other forms of capital consists on the evidence that the physical capital and the human capital can easily be acquired from other firms, while the organizational capital has to be generated inside the firm, i.e., it just cannot be imported from outside because the specific language that the firm develops cannot be transmitted without losing a large part of its value and effectiveness. The language is a property of the firm, it is a code that cannot be easily converted into another environment, even though some of the individuals of one organization move together to another firm.

The organizational capital has implications in the way firms manage their human resources. Since this form of capital implies an accumulation process over time through interaction and sharing of experiences, changes in work teams can influence the capacity to accumulate this special type of input. If it is true that sometimes organizational change brings some kind of advantage (when it leads to an efficient reallocation of resources), the undertaken changes, namely in what concerns the allocation of human capital, can imply a destruction of the organizational capital. In the model to develop in this chapter, the destruction of organizational capital will be taken into account; a depreciation variable concerning this form of capital will translate the loss of human resources by the firm that were important in the dissemination of the language and also the obstacles in transmitting the language among different generations of workers.

Benkard (1999) approaches the organizational capital depreciation issue. The firms that better accomplish the transmission of the organization's language to their new collaborators will be the firms that less organizational capital will lose with the exit of the ones working in the organization for a long time and that therefore were nuclear elements in maintaining the integrity of this form of capital.

Synthesizing, firms manage their activity oriented to a specific goal: profit maximization. This requires the accumulation of production factors, through investment; among the production factors we find the trivial ones, i.e., physical capital and human capital, as well as several kinds of intangible assets. Besides these factors, the firm also accumulates organizational capital. The accumulation of this form of capital possesses, then, some peculiar characteristics:

(i) The investment in organizational capital is made through a communication process specifically oriented to such end and consists on the creation of an internal language;

(ii) The internal language that the corporate communication creates is not dissociable from the firm itself: it cannot be transmitted or relocated across firms and it is difficult to replicate;

(iii) The accumulation of organizational capital implies a certain stability on management, working procedures, employees, ... The firm will not be interested in sudden changes because they tend to destroy the value of the internal language; likewise, the worker will lose when leaving the firm, since the internal language that she shared will have no use in her new functions;

(iv) All firms develop a language. The main question relates to whether the firm is making an oriented effort in order for the organizational culture and language to be developed with the purpose of obtaining the desired results;

(v) Communication and language are mutually reinforcing: without communication, a language capable of producing positive results, is not developed; once a language that contributes to a solid organizational culture is developed, the communication of ideas becomes more effective.

As in the previous chapters, we intend to develop here a model capable of furnishing a formal explanation for the most relevant features of the specific communication process in consideration.[1] Also as in the other chapters, this is a limited explanation that focuses in a specific point. Basically, one intends to discuss the profit maximization problem of the firm when it accumulates different forms of capital, including organizational capital. The fact that the firm makes a purposive effort in investment in communication will be the central element of the mechanism to be developed. We will focus the attention on a single firm, and therefore the model will be unable to address the issue of organizational capital specificity (i.e., the issue relating the difficulties of transferring this form of capital from one place to another or from one firm to another).

The chapter is organized in the following way. Section 4.1 formalizes the problem of intertemporal maximization for the profit maximizing firm. Section 4.2 adds to the analysis the organizational capita and introduces the assumption that a high quantity of organizational capital contributes for better results in terms of human capital accumulation. Section 4.3 undertakes the study of the dynamics underlying the specified model, with a special emphasis on the characterization of the long-run steady-state and on the way the convergence towards such point is attainable. Section 4.4 sophisticates the model by introducing a dynamic variable relating to the accumulation of physical capital. Finally, section 4.5 presents some applications.

4.1. THE FIRM'S PROBLEM

A firm exists in order to manage the production of a given good or service. To the firm belongs the responsibility of combining the productive inputs to which it has access to, in the most efficient possible way, in order to generate a level of production that, once costs of

---

1 The model develops with greater detail the theoretical structure presented in Gomes (2007).

production are accounted for (i.e., the costs of production inputs), should be the highest possible. As referred in the introduction, the firm directs its activity to the maximization of profits.

Consider a firm that has access to a given technological level, which we consider constant, $A>0$. For this technology index, the firm combines productive inputs and as a result obtains a determined level of output / income, $Y(t)$. This notion defines a production function; in analytical terms such function is presented as

$$Y(t) = A.f[K(t), H(t)] \qquad (4.1)$$

In (4.1), $K(t)$ defines the physical capital input and $H(t)$ will be the variable that represents the quantity of human capital held by the firm at a given moment t. Note the difference in nature of the capital variables, on one hand, and of the generated income, on the other; income is a flow variable (it corresponds to the flow of income generated at each time period); the capital variables are stock variables, in the sense that they represent values that are accumulated in time by the firm, through an investment process.

The similarity between physical capital and human capital is found on the fact that they are both the result of an investment process. The difference consists on the fact that the first capital variable respects to physical goods that allow producing additional goods, while the second variable corresponds to the human capabilities with value added by education and by learning-by-doing processes.

A production function as (4.1) furnishes a dynamic process where uncertainty is absent; a given quantity of capital is introduced into the system and, given the state of technology, the generated level of output will immediately be known with full certainty. This completely deterministic view on the production process, similar to the one adopted for communication in previous chapters, is a required simplification to characterize the dynamics of the model.

The properties of the production function are fundamental in what concerns the type of dynamic behavior to obtain. A common specification is the neoclassical production function. A neoclassical production function will exhibit positive and diminishing marginal returns for both its productive inputs: $\frac{\partial f}{\partial K} > 0$, $\frac{\partial^2 f}{\partial K^2} < 0$, $\frac{\partial f}{\partial H} > 0$ and $\frac{\partial^2 f}{\partial H^2} < 0$. These conditions imply that additional units of any of the production factors, maintaining the quantity of the other input constant, production will increase, but progressively less: each additional unit of physical capital or of human capital will contribute to additional production but the marginal contribution will decrease with the accumulation of inputs by the firm.

Another important property of the production functions (not only of the neoclassical type) is that both inputs are essential to production at each time moment; if the level of one of the forms of capital used in production is zero the result of production will be zero, even if the endowment of the other input is high.

Besides the previous properties, the production function also exhibits constant returns to scale; this assumption implies that we are working with a perfect competition environment, in which the scale of production is irrelevant and therefore no tendency for market concentration exists. Constant returns to scale imply that a change in the scale of production will lead to a change of equal value in the production outcome. By a change in the scale of production we mean the change, in equal proportion, on the quantities of inputs that are used in production.

The hypothesis of constant returns to scale is mathematically translated on a homogeneous of degree 1 production function; for a given constant $\tau > 0$,

$$f[\tau.K(t), \tau.H(t)] = \tau.f[K(t), H(t)] \tag{4.2}$$

In a first phase, we will concentrate attention exclusively on the human capital variable; thus, we will assume that the physical capital stock will grow at a constant rate, $\gamma > 0$. In this case, the production function can be rewritten in the following form:

$$Y(t) = A.f[\kappa.e^{\gamma.t}, H(t)] \tag{4.3}$$

In (4.3), parameter κ corresponds to the initial value of the physical capital variable.

Given the properties of the neoclassical production function, it will be convenient to present it under a specific functional form. The following function, generally known as Cobb-Douglas production function, obeys to the set of requirements one as presented above,

$$Y(t) = A.\kappa^{1-\mu}.e^{\gamma.(1-\mu).t}.H(t)^{\mu} \tag{4.4}$$

Parameter μ is defined on the interval $(0,1)$ and corresponds to the output - human capital elasticity (percentage change on the level of output arising from a unit percentage change in the level of human capital); obviously, $1-\mu$ will be the output – physical capital elasticity.

In order to simplify the presentation of the production function, we can define variables output per unit of physical capital and human capital per unit of physical capital; the adoption of these relative variables does not change significantly the interpretation of the values of the variables because physical capital will grow at a constant rate over time. Let $y(t) \equiv Y(t)/K(t)$ and $h(t) \equiv H(t)/K(t)$. The production function is now presented in intensive form,

$$y(t) = A.h(t)^{\mu} \tag{4.5}$$

Production function (4.5) obeys to the neoclassical properties, i.e., it is an increasing function [positive first derivative: $\dfrac{dy}{dh} = \mu.A.h(t)^{-(1-\mu)}$], and concave relatively to the horizontal axis [negative second derivative: $\dfrac{d^2 y}{\partial h^2} = -(1-\mu).\mu.A.h(t)^{-(2-\mu)}$].

Production function (4.5) corresponds to the income that the firm's activity can generate, by unit of physical capital. Besides the generated income, the firm has costs associated to its activity, namely the costs relating to the investment that is undertaken in the accumulation of productive inputs. Let $I_k(t)$ be the variable of physical capital investment and $I_h(t)$ the variable relating investment in human capital.

The increase in the quantities of physical and human capital that the activity of the firm suffers at each time moment will correspond to the investment that is made in each capital form, relatively to which is necessary to deduct the corresponding depreciation. Being δ_k and δ_h the depreciation rates of physical and human capital, respectively, the following differential equations reflect the accumulation of each one of the inputs by the firm,

$$\dot{K}(t) = I_k(t) - \delta_k.K(t), \, K(0)=\kappa \text{ given} \tag{4.6}$$

$$\dot{H}(t) = I_h(t) - \delta_h.H(t), \, H(0)=H_0 \text{ given} \tag{4.7}$$

We define $i_k(t)$ as the investment in physical capital by unit of physical capital and $i_h(t)$ the investment in human capital per unit of human capital. Since one has assumed that physical capital grows in time at constant rate γ, given (4.6), this means that $i_k(t)=\gamma+\delta_k$, i.e., the investment in physical capital per unit of physical capital already accumulated by the firm is constant. On the other hand, considering (4.6) and (4.7), it is possible to present the following equation relating the time evolution of the human capital stock by unit of physical capital,

$$\dot{h}(t) = \left[i_h(t) - \delta_h - \gamma \right] h(t) \tag{4.8}$$

The production costs of the firm correspond, then, to the investment levels in both forms of capital. Thus, one can present the profit of the firm through the following expression,

$$\Pi(t) \equiv Y(t) - I_k(t) - I_h(t) \tag{4.9}$$

The firm's profit will correspond to the income obtained with production less the corresponding investment costs. Expression (4.9) can give place to a definition of profit per unit of physical capital [$\pi(t) \equiv \Pi(t)/K(t)$], and therefore we can write

$$\pi(t) \equiv A.h(t)^{\mu} - \gamma - \delta_k - i_h(t).h(t) \tag{4.10}$$

In (4.10), given that the variables are presented in units of physical capital, only two endogenous variables arise as relevant in the profit expression: the quantity of human capital, $h(t)$, and the investment in this form of capital, $i_h(t)$. For now, we will evaluate the model taking into account just these two variables.

We are considering an intertemporal model; consecutive time moments are assumed. The problem of the firm consists then, at time $t=0$, in defining the optimal human capital investment strategy in order to maximize profits in an intertemporal perspective. Considering a rate of intertemporal discount $\rho > 0$, according to which the firm weights strongly profits in the near future than future profits in a more distant future, and taking an infinite horizon (absence of an expectation regarding the end of the life of the firm's activity), the problem of the firm will be:

$$Max \int_0^{+\infty} \pi(t).e^{-\rho.t}.dt \text{ subject to (4.8)} \tag{4.11}$$

The optimal control problem (4.11) describes the intention of the firm in choosing the level of investment in human capital (which is a control variable), in order to attain the desired objective, which is the maximization of profits in an intertemporal perspective.

Solving problem (4.11) requires a same type of techniques used in the previous chapter. First, we present a Hamiltonian function that takes a shadow-price $p_h(t)$,

$$\aleph(t) \equiv \pi(t) + p_h(t).[i_h(t) - \delta_h - \gamma]h(t) \tag{4.12}$$

In what follows, we compute the optimality necessary conditions:

$$\aleph_{i_h} = 0 \Rightarrow p_h(t) = 1 \tag{4.13}$$

$$\dot{p}_h(t) = [\rho + \delta_h + \gamma - i_h(t)]p_h(t) - \mu.A.h(t)^{-(1-\mu)} + i_h(t) \tag{4.14}$$

$$\lim_{t \to +\infty} p_h(t).e^{-\rho.t}.h(t) = 0 \text{ (transversality condition)} \tag{4.15}$$

According with (4.13), the shadow-price is constant and equal to 1. This means that the expression (4.14) can be transformed in order to encounter a constant value $h(t)$ that is valid for all moments of time. In concrete, one obtains

$$h(t) = \left(\frac{\mu.A}{\rho + \delta_h + \gamma} \right)^{1/(1-\mu)} \tag{4.16}$$

Result (4.16) indicates that the process of maximization produces a constant value in time for the variable human capital per physical capital unit and, therefore, the dynamic Equation (4.8) no longer makes sense. We also notice that the investment in human capital (per unit of human capital) is also a constant value: $i_h(t)=\gamma+\delta_h$. As in the case of physical capital, also the quantity of human capital grows at a constant rate, which corresponds to the value of investment found after withdrawing the depreciation rate of human capital.

In the scenario of profit maximization, one observes that no dynamics is associated to the model: the endogenous variables will assume constant values. The optimal profit (by physical capital unit) will be identical at all the time moments and will be given by expression (4.10), after replacing the optimal results of the variables; undertaking the corresponding computation,

$$\pi(t) = A^{1/(1-\mu)} \left(\frac{\mu}{\rho + \gamma + \delta_h} \right)^{\mu/(1-\mu)} \left[1 - (\gamma + \delta_h) \left(\frac{\mu}{\rho + \gamma + \delta_h} \right) \right] - \gamma - \delta_k \tag{4.17}$$

The optimal profit value will be influenced by several factors, namely it will increase with an improvement in the technological conditions and with a decrease in the value of the marginal returns on human capital (increase in μ); profit will decrease, at each time moment, as a function of the positive change in each one of the other assumed parameters.

The truly relevant point on this analysis is that the process of intertemporal profit maximization of the firm will imply, under the advanced simple assumptions, the absence of any dynamic process: the firm will invest always a same fraction of the already accumulated capital and the human capital – physical capital ratio will remain unchanged over time. As a result, profits per unit of physical capital will also be constant in time. All the variables expressed in absolute values, i.e., $\Pi(t)$, $K(t)$, $H(t)$, $I_k(t)$ and $I_h(t)$ grow in time at the same mentioned rate, γ.

In this model, we can determine the wage rate at which human capital is remunerated. The return on the human capital input (per unit of physical capital) will correspond to the marginal product of human capital, that is, to the derivative of (4.5) relatively to its single variable, $h(t)$. Replacing in this marginal product the optimal result (4.16), we observe that the following value corresponds to the wage rate:

$$w(t) = \frac{dy}{dh} = \rho + \gamma + \delta_h \qquad (4.18)$$

In the next section, we introduce a new form of capital, the organizational capital. With this form of capital, one intends not only to highlight once again the relevance of communication in achieving the goal of maximizing the profit of the firm, but also to introduce an element that will allow for a truly dynamic analysis, similar to the ones we have pursued in the previous chapters. Organizational capital will be modelled in such a way that the various variables of the model will not grow at constant rates at every time moment, being possible to discuss transitional dynamics and steady-state outcomes.

4.2. ORGANIZATIONAL CAPITAL

Let us return to the notion of organizational capital. Although corporate communication contributes in many ways to the formation of organizational capital, we are not able to address all these ways in our simple model; the analysis will be restricted to addressing the following ideas:

a) Corporate communication is oriented to the accumulation of organizational capital; there is an investment process in this form of capital, which is similar to the investment process considered in the previous section for human capital. As for human capital, this process of investment will have associated costs: the firm invests in communication in order to develop a language that constitutes its organizational capital;

b) The organizational capital does not contribute directly to the productive result; we assume, in the considered theoretical structure, that organizational capital contributes to the formation of human capital. The richer is the firm's language, the more the investment in human capital will allow generating additional human capital. For instance, a given formative action within the firm (that we can consider as investment in human capital) will produce as much additional human capital as the higher is the value of the organizational capital; in other words, the formative action will have obviously a higher degree of success if from the start the workers of the firm share a same set of symbols, that is, if they share a same language and a same organizational culture.

The above two points give the required guidance to formulate the intertemporal problem of the firm in the presence of accumulation of organizational capital through internal communication. The most evident consequence is that a dynamic analysis becomes feasible; the several variables will no longer grow exactly at the same rate over time.

Let $O(t)$ be the organizational capital variable. The value of $O(t)$ will be as much higher as the more the firm invests in communication and, therefore, it makes sense to write an accumulation equation similar to (4.6) and (4.7). Being $I_o(t)$ the investment in organizational capital and δ_o the rate of depreciation of this form of capital, one can present the following dynamic equation,

$$\dot{O}(t) = I_o(t) - \delta_o.O(t), \ O(0)=O_0 \text{ given} \tag{4.19}$$

As in the case of human capital accumulation, Equation (4.19) can be written taking the variable organizational capital – physical capital ratio; let $o(t) \equiv O(t)/K(t)$ and $i_o(t) \equiv I_o(t)/O(t)$. Similarly to (4.8), we will have

$$\dot{o}(t) = \left[i_o(t) - \delta_o - \gamma \right] o(t) \tag{4.20}$$

Communication consists in the way in which the investment in organizational capital is materialized. Making this investment will be a cost to the firm, and therefore we must weight it in the profit function. We continue to assume that the production is made by resorting to physical and to human capital inputs, implying that the profit function per unit of physical capital will correspond to (4.10) subtracted by the term that corresponds to the investment in organizational capital.

$$\pi(t) \equiv A.h(t)^\mu - \gamma - \delta_k - i_h(t).h(t) - i_o(t).o(t) \tag{4.21}$$

The main question we are faced with is why the firm invests in communication, if this represents a cost and the result of the communication process does not allow generating any direct productive result. The answer resides on the assumption that a high level of organizational capital contributes in a direct way to a more effective accumulation of human capital, with this last one the input that directly serves the productive activity. Analytically, we will translate this last assumption on the idea that investment in human capital will benefit from the existence of organizational capital in order to generate additional human capital, i.e.,

$$\dot{H}(t) = I_h(t).o(t)^\varepsilon - \delta_h.H(t) \qquad (4.22)$$

With (4.22), one changes the human capital accumulation Equation (4.7), by indicating that the accumulation of human capital is not exclusively a function of the investment made in this form of capital, but also of the accumulated organizational capital (per unit of physical capital). In this model, the communication inside the firm serves a specific purpose: to turn more efficient the accumulation of human skills, which are indispensable in order to obtain good productive results.

Parameter $\varepsilon \in (0,1)$ translates the presence of diminishing marginal returns of the organizational capital over the accumulation of human capital. This means that the larger is the stock of accumulated organizational capital, the less effective will be the result of communication over the accumulation of human capital; additional organizational capital contributes always to increase the human capital stock, but these increases tend to become progressively smaller.

Equation (4.22) can be rewritten in order to reveal the time movement of the human capital per unit of physical capital variable. We will have,

$$\dot{h}(t) = \left[i_h(t).o(t)^\varepsilon - \delta_h - \gamma\right]h(t) \qquad (4.23)$$

The firm's problem when it invests in organizational capital is now completely defined: it is a problem of intertemporal optimization, involving an infinite horizon and considering a rate of discount of future profits, $\rho>0$, where one maximizes over time the series of functions (4.21), with the maximization problem subject to two constraints, (4.20) and (4.23). Once again, we can highlight the indirect role that communication has in order to stimulate production and to obtain higher profits: a good communication (that allows to accumulate organizational capital) will imply that the workers in the organization will be able to learn tasks more easily, i.e., any investment process the firm makes in order to generate value will lead to higher rewards when the developed language is more efficient.

To solve the model, one follows the same steps as in the previous chapter. We begin by presenting the current value Hamiltonian function, with $p_h(t)$ and $p_o(t)$ the shadow-prices of each capital variable.

$$\aleph(t) \equiv \pi(t) + p_h(t).\left[i_h(t).o(t)^\varepsilon - \delta_h - \gamma\right]h(t)$$
$$+ p_o(t).\left[i_o(t) - \delta_o - \gamma\right]o(t) \qquad (4.24)$$

Again, one needs to compute the necessary optimality conditions. Given the profit maximization problem, the following conditions are derived:

$$\aleph_{i_h} = 0 \Rightarrow p_h(t) = o(t)^{-\varepsilon} \qquad (4.25)$$

$$\aleph_{i_o} = 0 \Rightarrow p_o(t) = 1 \qquad (4.26)$$

$$\dot{p}_h(t) = \left[\rho + \delta_h + \gamma - i_h(t).o(t)^\varepsilon\right] p_h(t) - \mu.A.h(t)^{-(1-\mu)} + i_h(t) \tag{4.27}$$

$$\dot{p}_o(t) = \left[\rho + \delta_o + \gamma - i_o(t)\right] p_o(t) - \varepsilon.i_h(t).h(t).o(t)^{-(1-\varepsilon)}.p_h(t) + i_o(t) \tag{4.28}$$

$$\lim_{t \to +\infty} p_h(t).e^{-\rho.t}.h(t) = 0 \text{ (transversality condition)} \tag{4.29}$$

$$\lim_{t \to +\infty} p_o(t).e^{-\rho.t}.o(t) = 0 \text{ (transversality condition)} \tag{4.30}$$

The optimal control problem has twice the dimension of the problem described in the previous section, where no organizational capital was considered. Thus, the number of optimality conditions also doubles. By taking in consideration conditions (4.25) to (4.28) one can derive a system of dynamic equations through which it is possible to study the mechanics underlying the model.

Condition (4.26) allows simplifying (4.28). Given that the shadow-price of organizational capital is equal to one, relation (4.28) is reduced to a static relation. Taking in consideration (4.25) this will be:

$$i_h(t) = \frac{\rho + \delta_o + \gamma}{\varepsilon}.\frac{o(t)}{h(t)} \tag{4.31}$$

Expression (4.21) furnishes an optimal result for the investment in human capital at each time moment. This investment variable will increase in value with a rise on the accumulated level of organizational capital and with a fall on the stock of human capital.

To continue with the dynamic analysis we differentiate (4.25) with respect to time; one obtains,

$$\dot{p}_h(t) = -\varepsilon.o(t)^{-1-\varepsilon}.\dot{o}(t) \tag{4.32}$$

Replacing in (4.32) the variation of the shadow-price of capital by the corresponding optimal result in (4.27), one determines a differential equation representing the motion of the organizational capital by unit of physical capital variable. Obtaining such equation also requires the replacement of the investment in human capital by the corresponding value in (4.31). Differential Equation (4.33) is derived,

$$\dot{o}(t) = \frac{\mu}{\varepsilon}.A.h(t)^{-(1-\mu)}.o(t)^{1+\varepsilon} - \frac{\rho + \delta_h + \gamma}{\varepsilon}.o(t) \tag{4.33}$$

Equation (4.33) describes the motion in time of the organizational capital per unit of physical capital variable as a function of this same variable and of the variable human capital per unit of physical capital. One can also present the differential equation relating the change on the value of human capital as a function just of capital variables. Replacing (4.31) in (4.23), one obtains

$$\dot{h}(t) = \frac{\rho + \delta_o + \gamma}{\varepsilon} . o(t)^{1+\varepsilon} - (\delta_h + \gamma).h(t)$$

(4.34)

Equation (4.34) presents the variation of variable $h(t)$, as a function of this same variable and of the organizational capital per physical capital unit.

As one observes, Equations (4.33) and (4.34) form a two equations system with two endogenous variables; in this way, the dynamic analysis of the model is reduced to the observation of the dynamics that this pair of variables encloses. First, one will characterize the long-run steady-state and following this we linearize the system in the vicinity of the equilibrium; the linearization procedure allows describing the dynamics of the system by building a phase diagram or by computing the eigenvalues of the Jacobian matrix of the system. In section 4.3 one pursues a detailed analysis of the local dynamic properties of the model.

4.3. EQUILIBRIUM AND DYNAMICS

The characterization of the steady-state of the profit maximization problem of the firm when this invests in internal communication will allow to find long-term results for accumulated capital values and for the investment flows concerning each one of the assumed capital forms. Solving system $[\dot{h}(t), \dot{o}(t)] = (0,0)$ it is straightforward to obtain equilibrium values for the capital variables:

$$\bar{o} = \left[\frac{A}{\varepsilon} . \frac{\rho + \delta_o + \gamma}{\rho + \delta_h + \gamma} . \frac{1}{\delta_h + \gamma} \right]^{1/[1 - \mu.(1+\varepsilon)]} \quad ; \quad \bar{h} = \frac{\rho + \delta_o + \gamma}{\varepsilon.(\delta_h + \gamma)} . \bar{o}^{1+\varepsilon}$$

(4.35)

The steady-state results (4.35) guarantee the existence of a unique steady-state in which the accumulation of any of the forms of capital (physical, human or organizational) occurs at a same rate γ. This conclusion is a consequence of the ratios between capital forms being, in the equilibrium, constant values.

Also the investment in each type of capital will grow, in the long-run, at the same rate γ. Thus, the ratios $i_h(t)$ and $i_o(t)$ will also be constant in the steady-state. The equilibrium values are:

$$\bar{i}_h = \frac{\rho + \delta_o + \gamma}{\varepsilon} . \frac{\bar{o}}{\bar{h}} \quad ; \quad \bar{i}_o = \delta_o + \gamma$$

(4.36)

The equilibrium value of investment in human capital is directly computable from (4.31). The steady-state value of the organizational capital investment is found by resorting to (4.20).

Results (4.35) and (4.36) furnish a unique steady-state point of dimension four, in which the various defined coefficients assume constant values; this means that all the original variables [capital forms, $K(t)$, $H(t)$, $O(t)$, and investment flows, $I_k(t)$, $I_h(t)$, $I_o(t)$] grow in the long-run at the same rate γ. The difference between this model and the version of profit maximization without investment in communication is that now this result is restricted to the equilibrium solution, while in the original version of the model the stated result was obtained at every time moment.

A relevant question in the present context is whether the investment in communication is profitable and in which circumstances is it profitable, under a long-run perspective. For the model without investment in communication and accumulation of organizational capital, one has observed that the profit per unit of physical capital corresponds to the value in expression (4.17); this would be a constant value in time, and therefore the profit would vary exclusively as a result of a change on the accumulated level of physical capital, which is a variable that is exogenous to our analysis.

In the new model, with investment in communication, the profit expression is (4.21), but this no longer corresponds to a constant value over time. Because the various variables possess constant values in the long-run it is feasible to present a constant value for $\pi(t)$. Replacing the various steady-state results in (4.21), one observes that

$$\overline{\pi} = \frac{(\rho+\delta_o).\rho-(\delta_o+\delta_h).\gamma-\varepsilon.(\delta_o+\gamma).(\delta_h+\gamma)}{\varepsilon.(\delta_h+\gamma)}.\overline{o}-\gamma-\delta_k \qquad (4.37)$$

To verify if the investment in organizational capital is advantageous in the steady-state it is necessary to compare (4.37) with (4.17). Given the complexity of the expressions, this comparison does not generate an unequivocal result. Intuition tells us that (4.37) should be a higher value; after all, we are working with optimization scenarios, and therefore the introduction of an additional control variable (the investment in organizational capital) constitutes one more element that can be manipulated in order to achieve the highest possible profit level.

In the scenario without investment in communication one has determined the value of the average wage rate that the firm pays and one has verified that this is a constant in time value, given by (4.18). The same computation may be undertaken for the model with communication, in what concerns the steady-state result. The wage rate corresponds to the derivative of the production function with respect to its single variable, the human capital (per unit of physical capital), i.e., the wage rate will be the marginal product of human capital. From condition (4.33) one understands that the equilibrium value of the referred marginal product corresponds to:

$$\overline{w} = \frac{dy}{dh} = \left(\rho+\gamma+\delta_h\right)\overline{o}^{-\varepsilon} \qquad (4.38)$$

The wage rate (4.38) is easily comparable with (4.18). The investment in organizational communication will allow for a higher wage rate if the steady-state value of the stock of organizational capital, (4.35), is an amount inferior to one.

Let us now inquire about the transitional dynamics towards the steady-state. First of all, one linearizes system (4.33)-(4.34) in the vicinity of the steady-state. The corresponding computation allows to present expression (4.39).

$$\begin{bmatrix} \dot{h}(t) \\ \dot{o}(t) \end{bmatrix} = J. \begin{bmatrix} h(t) - \overline{h} \\ o(t) - \overline{o} \end{bmatrix}$$

(4.39)

with

$$J = \begin{bmatrix} \dfrac{\partial \dot{h}(t)}{\partial h(t)}\bigg|_{(\overline{h},\overline{o})} & \dfrac{\partial \dot{h}(t)}{\partial o(t)}\bigg|_{(\overline{h},\overline{o})} \\[2ex] \dfrac{\partial \dot{o}(t)}{\partial h(t)}\bigg|_{(\overline{h},\overline{o})} & \dfrac{\partial \dot{o}(t)}{\partial o(t)}\bigg|_{(\overline{h},\overline{o})} \end{bmatrix}$$

$$= \begin{bmatrix} -(\delta_h + \gamma) & (1+\varepsilon).(\delta_h + \gamma).\dfrac{\overline{h}}{\overline{o}} \\[2ex] -(1-\mu).\dfrac{\rho + \delta_h + \gamma}{\varepsilon}.\dfrac{\overline{o}}{\overline{h}} & \rho + \delta_h + \gamma \end{bmatrix}$$

(4.40)

Once obtained the linearized system, the dynamic analysis may be undertaken both analytically and graphically. Let us start by the analytical approach. Trace and determinant of the Jacobian matrix are as follows: $Tr(J)=\rho$ and $Det(J) = \left[\dfrac{(1+\varepsilon).(1-\mu)}{\varepsilon} - 1 \right].(\rho + \delta_h + \gamma).(\delta_h + \gamma)$. The trace is a positive value, what excludes from the start the possibility of both eigenvalues being negative and, therefore, excludes the scenario of overall stability. The only possibility of having a stable outcome will correspond to a saddle-path equilibrium, which will exist only if the determinant of J is a negative value. Therefore, the stability of the equilibrium will require the satisfaction of the following condition: $\dfrac{(1+\varepsilon).(1-\mu)}{\varepsilon} < 1$. Parameters ε and μ must be such that the previous condition holds; simplifying, one observes the need to impose the following constraint on parameter values in order to obtain a saddle-path equilibrium:

$$\varepsilon > \frac{1-\mu}{\mu}$$

(4.41)

If condition (4.41) is satisfied, one will have a steady-state point that is saddle-path stable; otherwise, the equilibrium will be impossible to be reached and the firm will not attain the desired profit level. Figure 4.1 represents, on the space of parameters ε and μ, the stable sub-space; this is represented in grey. Below and to the left of the drawn space, the steady-state is unstable.

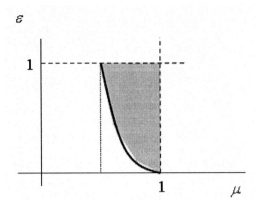

Figure 4.1. Relation between parameters ε and μ allowing for the existence of a saddle-path stable equilibrium.

In the following analysis, we consider that (4.41) is verified, i.e., that the decreasing returns on organizational capital over the accumulation of human capital are not too pronounced in order to prevent the existence of a saddle trajectory. In this way, one can determine the analytical expression of the stable trajectory, resorting for such to the computation of the eigenvector associated to the negative eigenvalue of matrix J.

For an eigenvector $P_1 = [p_{11} \ p_{21}]$, in which p_{21} is equal to 1, element p_{11} will be given by

expression $p_{11} = \dfrac{\varepsilon.(\rho + \delta_h + \gamma - \lambda_1)}{(1 - \mu).(\rho + \delta_h + \gamma)} \cdot \dfrac{\overline{h}}{\overline{o}}$. In the expression, λ_1 respects to the negative

eigenvalue. The slope of the saddle-path will correspond to the inverse of p_{11}, with this a positive value; one finds a relation of adjustment towards the steady-state of the same sign between variables $h(t)$ and $o(t)$. The expression of the stable trajectory is, then,

$$o(t) = \left[1 - \frac{(1 - \mu).(\rho + \delta_h + \gamma)}{\varepsilon.(\rho + \delta_h + \gamma - \lambda_1)} \right].\overline{o} + \frac{(1 - \mu).(\rho + \delta_h + \gamma)}{\varepsilon.(\rho + \delta_h + \gamma - \lambda_1)} \cdot \frac{\overline{o}}{\overline{h}}.h(t) \qquad (4.42)$$

The same stable trajectory can be graphically presented through the construction of a phase diagram. The following equations correspond to the isoclines:

$$\dot{h}(t) = 0 \Rightarrow o(t) - \overline{o} = \frac{1}{1 - \varepsilon} \cdot \frac{\overline{o}}{\overline{h}}.\left[h(t) - \overline{h} \right];$$

$$\dot{o}(t) = 0 \Rightarrow o(t) - \overline{o} = \frac{1 - \mu}{\varepsilon} \cdot \frac{\overline{o}}{\overline{h}}.\left[h(t) - \overline{h} \right].$$

Both isoclines have a positive slope, with condition (4.41) guaranteeing that the slope of the first is larger than the slope of the second. The elements in the first column of the Jacobian matrix are both negative, and therefore they indicate that the directional arrows point to the left at the right of $\dot{h}(t) = 0$ and to the right in the opposite case, and they point down to the right of $\dot{o}(t) = 0$, and point up to the left of this isocline. We can then represent the phase diagram and the directional arrows indicating the dynamics of the system.

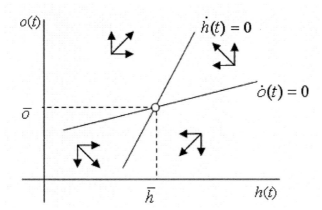

Figure 4.2. Phase diagram in the profit maximization model, with investment in communication.

Figure 4.2 points as possible location for the stable trajectory the region where, having a positive slope, the line in consideration displays a lower inclination than isocline $\dot{o}(t) = 0$. Recovering (4.42) and comparing the slope of the stable trajectory with the one of the mentioned isocline, one confirms this result: the saddle-trajectory has a positive slope but lower than the one of any of the isoclines. The low inclination of the saddle trajectory signifies that, in the convergence to equilibrium, large variations on the quantity of human capital are associated with small changes on the stock of organizational capital; this will be an argument in favour of the investment in communication by the organizations, since with a small increase in organizational capital one achieves a significant growth on the quantity of human capital that is available to generate income.

Note as well what an instability result represents in this case; according to the directional arrows in the graphic of figure 4.2, the unstable or anti-saddle trajectory will also be positively sloped, but with a slope larger than the ones of any of the isoclines. Thus, for initial levels of organizational capital and human capital below the equilibrium ones, to follow an unstable trajectory will mean to the firm, in the long-run, the absence of accumulation of organizational capital and the accumulation of human capital in a quantity that is inferior to the equilibrium one. Instability means, in this analytical structure, that the firm cannot make from communication an instrument able of promoting human capital efficiency, and therefore the effort put into communication will be abandoned and the model will be reduced to the mechanics discussed in section 4.1.

To close this section, one explores the effect of exogenous perturbations over the steady-state. Equations (4.33) and (4.34) involve a significant set of exogenous variables: the technology associated to the production activity, the constant values that represent the decreasing returns of organizational capital over production and over the accumulation of human capital, discount rate of future profits, the growth rate of physical capital and the depreciation rates of human capital and organizational capital.

As an illustration, one analyzes the impact of a perturbation on the depreciation rate of the organizational capital over the characterized steady-state. Organizational capital depreciates when, by any reason, the language of the firm loses influence and additional obstacles exist to its understanding. The way in which the firm is managed will be a determinant factor for the value that this rate assumes; the more or less frequent change in the allocation of employees to certain tasks or working places, the policy regarding the entrance and the exit of workers in the firm and the way in which the employers change their attitudes and behavior towards employees, are all elements that may contribute to change the value of the rate at which the organizational capital depreciates.

One does not intend to turn this rate endogenous, even because most of the factors determining it are external to the firm and escape its control. Nevertheless, one can assume for instance a negative shock on the value of this parameter, which can be interpreted as the result of a series of measures taken by the firm's managers in order to reduce the loss of organizational capital at each time moment.

In a first phase, the analysis of this perturbation requires the computation of the perturbation vector, which is,

$$J(\delta_o) = \begin{bmatrix} \dfrac{\partial \dot{h}(t)}{\partial \delta_o(t)}\bigg|_{(\bar{h},\bar{o})} \\[2ex] \dfrac{\partial \dot{o}(t)}{\partial \delta_o(t)}\bigg|_{(\bar{h},\bar{o})} \end{bmatrix} = \begin{bmatrix} \dfrac{\delta_h + \gamma}{\rho + \delta_o + \gamma}.\bar{h} \\[2ex] 0 \end{bmatrix}$$

(4.43)

The perturbation vector allows to find the effects of the disturbance $\Delta \delta_o$; now the procedure is not identical to the one in the previous chapter for the model of optimization of the communication result, since in the present case one is not considering a state variable and a control variable; both capital variables are state variables, implying that any initial jump triggered by the change in the value of the parameter is simply absent. Both capital variables will converge simultaneously from the first to the second equilibrium.

The long-run impact of the perturbation requires the determination of the inverse of the Jacobian matrix (4.40). This is

$$J^{-1} = \frac{1}{Det(J)}.\begin{bmatrix} \rho + \delta_h + \gamma & -\dfrac{1-\mu}{\varepsilon}.(\rho+\delta_h+\gamma).\dfrac{\bar{o}}{\bar{h}} \\[2ex] -(1+\varepsilon).(\delta_h+\gamma).\dfrac{\bar{h}}{\bar{o}} & -\delta_h - \gamma \end{bmatrix}$$

(4.44)

The intended long-run effects correspond to:

$$\begin{bmatrix} \Delta \bar{h}_\infty \\ \Delta \bar{o}_\infty \end{bmatrix} = -J^{-1} . J(\delta_0) . \Delta^- \delta_o$$

$$= \frac{1}{Det(J)} . \begin{bmatrix} -(\delta_h + \gamma) . \bar{h} \\ (1+\varepsilon) . \dfrac{(\delta_h + \gamma)^2}{\rho + \delta_h + \gamma} . \dfrac{\bar{h}^2}{\bar{o}} \end{bmatrix} . \Delta^- \delta_o \tag{4.45}$$

Since the determinant of the Jacobian matrix will be, in the present case, a negative value, one concludes that a decrease in the depreciation rate of organizational capital will provoke a fall in the steady-state value of the human capital variable and an increase in the steady-state value of organizational capital. The equilibrium values (4.35) allow confirming this result, when to them one applies the referred perturbation.

4.4. PHYSICAL CAPITAL ACCUMULATION

Until now, the accumulation of physical capital was considered exogenous. The firm invests in each period of time an amount of income in physical capital, which will correspond to the sum of two values: the value that is needed to recover the depreciated capital and a second amount relating to the net growth on the quantity of available capital.

In this section, we consider the physical capital as an endogenous variable, having the firm the possibility to manage the investment in this form of capital as an additional resource in order to optimize the result of the problem it needs to solve. The problem of the firm consists, now, in maximizing profits as given by

$$\Pi(t) \equiv A.K(t)^{1-\mu} . H(t)^{\mu} - I_k(t) - I_h(t) - I_o(t) \tag{4.46}$$

The maximization of (4.46) is, once again, undertaken under an infinite horizon and assuming a same discount rate of future profits as the one considered in previous sections. The constraints on the maximization problem are (4.6), which, we recall, translates the process of physical capital accumulation, (4.19), which is a similar equation for the accumulation of organizational capital, and (4.22), an equation that translates the idea that the human capital accumulation benefits not only from investment in this form of capital but also from a spillover effect that the organizational capital produces; recall that in this equation we measure the organizational capital as a relative variable, i.e., one assumes that it is the organizational capital per unit of physical capital that contributes to the growth of the stock of human capital to use in production.

To analyze the model with endogenous physical capital we will work with the variables in their original form. To the problem, corresponds the following current value Hamiltonian function,

$$\aleph(t) \equiv \Pi(t) + p_K(t).[I_k(t) - \delta_k.K(t)] + p_O(t).[I_o(t) - \delta_o.O(t)]$$
$$+ p_H(t).\left[I_h(t).\left(\frac{O(t)}{K(t)}\right)^{\varepsilon} - \delta_h.H(t)\right]$$

(4.47)

Variables $p_K(t)$, $p_O(t)$ and $p_H(t)$ are shadow-prices respecting to each one of the capital variables. In this new version of the model, we have three state variables, which are the three capital variables; we have also three control variables, which are the three forms of investment. The optimality conditions will now correspond to three sets of three equations; namely, one obtains

$$\aleph_{I_K} = 0 \Rightarrow p_K(t) = 1$$

(4.48)

$$\aleph_{I_O} = 0 \Rightarrow p_O(t) = 1$$

(4.49)

$$\aleph_{I_H} = 0 \Rightarrow p_H(t) = \left[\frac{K(t)}{O(t)}\right]^{\varepsilon}$$

(4.50)

$$\dot{p}_K(t) = (\rho + \delta_k).p_K(t) - (1-\mu).A.\left[\frac{H(t)}{K(t)}\right]^{\mu}$$
$$- \varepsilon.\frac{I_h(t)}{K(t)}\left[\frac{O(t)}{K(t)}\right]^{\varepsilon}.p_H(t)$$

(4.51)

$$\dot{p}_H(t) = (\rho + \delta_h).p_H(t) - \mu.A.\left[\frac{K(t)}{H(t)}\right]^{1-\mu}$$

(4.52)

$$\dot{p}_O(t) = (\rho + \delta_o).p_O(t) - \varepsilon.\frac{I_h(t)}{O(t)}\left[\frac{O(t)}{K(t)}\right]^{\varepsilon}.p_H(t)$$

(4.53)

$$\lim_{t \to +\infty} p_K(t).e^{-\rho.t}.K(t) = 0 \text{ (transversality condition)}$$

(4.54)

$$\lim_{t \to +\infty} p_H(t).e^{-\rho.t}.H(t) = 0 \text{ (transversality condition)}$$

(4.55)

$$\lim_{t \to +\infty} p_O(t).e^{-\rho.t}.O(t) = 0 \text{ (transversality condition)}$$

(4.56)

Conditions (4.48) to (4.50) allow simplifying Equations (4.51) to (4.53). The following conditions hold under a profit maximization behavior of the firm,

$$I_h(t) = \frac{1-\mu}{\varepsilon}.A.K(t)^{1-\mu}.H(t)^\mu - \frac{1}{\varepsilon}.(\rho+\delta_k).K(t) \tag{4.57}$$

$$\dot{p}_H(t) = (\rho+\delta_h).\left[\frac{K(t)}{O(t)}\right]^\varepsilon - \mu.A.\left[\frac{K(t)}{H(t)}\right]^{1-\mu} \tag{4.58}$$

$$I_h(t) = \frac{1}{\varepsilon}.(\rho+\delta_o).O(t) \tag{4.59}$$

Equations (4.57) to (4.59) correspond to (4.51) to (4.53) after replacing the shadow-prices by the corresponding values in (4.51) to (4.53). One observes that only one of the differential equations remains as a motion relation; the others lead to two different conditions involving the optimal investment on human capital. Considering simultaneously expressions (4.57) and (4.59) it is revealed that there is an optimal combination of capital amounts that holds at every time period.

In turn, expression (4.58) can be simplified. Differentiating (4.50) with respect to time, one can eliminate the variation of the shadow-price in (4.58). The following relation holds,

$$\frac{\dot{O}(t)}{O(t)} - \frac{\dot{K}(t)}{K(t)} = \frac{\mu}{\varepsilon}.A.\left[\frac{K(t)}{H(t)}\right]^{1-\mu}.\left[\frac{O(t)}{K(t)}\right]^\varepsilon - \frac{1}{\varepsilon}.(\rho+\delta_h) \tag{4.60}$$

Expression (4.60) can be simplified through the replacement of the growth rate of variables organizational capital and physical capital by the corresponding definitions:

$$\frac{I_o(t)}{O(t)} - \frac{I_k(t)}{K(t)} = \frac{\mu}{\varepsilon}.A.\left[\frac{K(t)}{H(t)}\right]^{1-\mu}.\left[\frac{O(t)}{K(t)}\right]^\varepsilon - \frac{1}{\varepsilon}.(\rho+\delta_h) + \delta_o - \delta_k \tag{4.61}$$

From the optimality results one has withdrawn conditions (4.57), (4.59) and (4.61), all of them static relations between the various variables of investment and capital. However ,these conditions do not allow to find explicit results for each one of the variables simply as functions of the parameters, and this implies that differently from the model in section 4.1, the variables are not constant in time.

To study the dynamics of the model, we return to the scenario of capital variables per unit of physical capital: $h(t) \equiv H(t)/K(t)$ and $o(t) \equiv O(t)/K(t)$. With these, Equation (4.60) is written again, now as

$$\dot{o}(t) = \left[\frac{\mu}{\varepsilon}.A.h(t)^{-(1-\mu)}.o(t)^\varepsilon - \frac{1}{\varepsilon}.(\rho+\delta_h)\right].o(t) \tag{4.62}$$

For $h(t)$ it is not possible to present a differential equation where investment variables are absent, however the combination of (4.57) and (4.59) leads to

$$h(t) = \left[\frac{1}{(1-\mu).A}.[(\rho+\delta_k)+(\rho+\delta_o).o(t)]\right]^{1/\mu} \tag{4.63}$$

Replacing (4.63) in (4.62) we obtain a differential equation with a single endogenous variable, which will be the quantity of organizational capital. This equation is:

$$\dot{o}(t) = \left[\frac{\mu}{\varepsilon}.A\left[\frac{1}{(1-\mu)A}.[(\rho+\delta_k)+(\rho+\delta_o)o(t)]\right]^{-(1-\mu)/\mu}.o(t)^{\varepsilon} - \frac{1}{\varepsilon}.(\rho+\delta_h)\right]o(t) \tag{4.64}$$

The dynamics of (4.64) is not easy to address. Now the steady-state point may not be unique, given that it is the solution of the Equation (4.65).

$$\left(\frac{A}{\rho+\delta_h}\right)^{\mu/(1-\mu)}.\bar{o}^{\varepsilon.\mu/(1-\mu)} - \frac{\rho+\delta_o}{(1-\mu).A}.\bar{o} - \frac{\rho+\delta_k}{(1-\mu).A} = 0 \tag{4.65}$$

One can address the dynamics of the model mainly through particular cases; for example, by assuming $\varepsilon=(1-\mu)/\mu$, one observes that the equilibrium point is unique. Hence, the computation of the slope of the differential equation in the vicinity of the steady-state can be undertaken. If this value has a negative sign then the equilibrium is stable; otherwise it is unstable. The result will depend on specific values of parameters.

By considering that the firm in the rational development of its activity optimizes the investment in physical capital in the same way it does for the investment in human capital and in communication, we find relevant differences in the corresponding models. In the endogenous physical capital case, the dynamic process is reduced to a unique dimension but the possibility of multiple equilibria arises. Even if some constraint imposes a unique equilibrium, the complexity of the obtained differential equation prevents a clear revelation about the type of dynamics associated to the problem.

A difference between the two cases is that now, with endogenous physical capital, the existence of a saddle-path equilibrium is no longer possible, because even though the dimension of the problem has augmented (from two to three dimensions), in dynamic terms we end up with a single dimension. In this case, only two possibilities exist: stability or instability. Observe also that once determined the type of dynamics associated to the organizational capital per physical capital unit variable, the dynamics of the human capital per unit of physical capital variable is immediately known, given that, according to (4.63), variable $h(t)$ can be written as a function of $o(t)$.

If the two models, with exogenous and endogenous physical capital produce such different results, which model should we take to characterize the relevance of the investment in organizational capital? The model in this section is more complete and realistic in the sense that all the investment decisions of the firm are contemplated; however, based on the observation that firms often undertake, in a short-run perspective, actions destined to promote the quality of their human capital and adjust their communication strategies much more often than they change facilities or radically modify the set of machines and equipments they use to produce, it makes sense to assume a setting where communication and investment in human capital are jointly determined, independently of the decisions concerning the material resources that are required in order to produce.

Independently of the version of the problem one takes, one should look at the models in this chapter as a way to emphasize the role of internal communication within a firm. The adopted theoretical structure starts from assuming that communication does not contribute directly to production, independently of the good or service the firm produces; nevertheless, firms easily encounter reasons to create and systematically improve a goal oriented communication system. The communication process intends to create or reinforce the specific language of the firm; its main direct result is to turn more efficient any investment in human capital that is undertaken. If the workers of a firm share a given language or code, then any new stimulus received by the human capital will be absorbed in a faster, easier and more effective way, making the stock of human capital to grow and the contribution of this input to the generation of income to grow as well.

Therefore, communication generates organizational capital and this contributes to accumulate human capital. The firm will invest in communication only if the resources that it diverts from investment in other forms of capital to this end produce a rewarding result given its main goal: to maximize profits. By obtaining an equilibrium point with constant organizational and human capital levels, one finds a reasonable result: the investment in human capital must not be excessive in order not to compromise the investment in communication; and also the effort in generating an organizational language must not be such that it implies neglecting the investment in other forms of capital.

4.5. APPLICATIONS

Application 1

Consider the production function $Y(t) = A.\left\{a.K(t)^{\psi} + (1-a).H(t)^{\psi}\right\}^{1/\psi}$, in which $a \in (0,1)$ and ψ is also a positive constant with a value below one. A, $K(t)$ and $H(t)$ correspond, as in previous sections, to a technological index and to the accumulated quantities of physical and human capital, respectively.

a) Is the presented production function a neoclassical production function?
b) Solve the profit maximization problem of the firm for the given production function. Consider the absence of investment in organizational capital.

A. A Neoclassical Production Function?

A neoclassical production function is the one for which the marginal returns on the production inputs are positive and diminishing and the returns to scale are constant (the production function must be homogeneous of degree 1). We have also considered has a property of the neoclassical production function the fact that both inputs are essential to produce. This does not happen in the present case, since $H(t)=0 \Rightarrow Y(t) = A.a^{1/\psi}.K(t)$ and $K(t)=0 \Rightarrow Y(t) = A.(1-a)^{1/\psi}.H(t)$.

Nevertheless, in what concerns the two central properties of a neoclassical production function, these are verified:

(i) The marginal returns are positive:

$$\frac{\partial Y(t)}{\partial K(t)} = A.a.\{a + (1-a).K(t)^{-\psi}.H(t)^{\psi}\}^{(1-\psi)/\psi} > 0;$$

$$\frac{\partial Y(t)}{\partial H(t)} = A.(1-a).\{a.K(t)^{\psi}.H(t)^{-\psi} + (1-a)\}^{(1-\psi)/\psi} > 0.$$

(ii) The marginal returns are decreasing:

$$\frac{\partial^2 Y(t)}{\partial K(t)^2} =$$

$$-\psi.A.a.(1-a).\left[a + (1-a).K(t)^{-\psi}.H(t)^{\psi}\right]^{(1-2.\psi)/\psi}.K(t)^{-1-\psi}.H(t)^{\psi} < 0$$

$$\frac{\partial^2 Y(t)}{\partial H(t)^2} =$$

$$-\psi.A.a.(1-a).\left[a.K(t)^{\psi}.H(t)^{-\psi} + (1-a)\right]^{(1-\psi)/\psi}.K(t)^{\psi}.H(t)^{-1-\psi} < 0$$

(iii) The returns to scale are constant:

For any constant $\tau>0$ one observes that,

$$\tau.A.\{a.K(t)^{\psi} + (1-a).H(t)^{\psi}\}^{1/\psi} = A.\{a.[\tau.K(t)]^{\psi} + (1-a).[\tau.H(t)]^{\psi}\}^{1/\psi}$$

B. Solve the Profit Maximization Problem

In section 4.1 one has observed that the intertemporal profit maximization problem of the firm does not enclose any dynamic process. The human capital variable, per unit of physical capital, will be constant, i.e., human capital and physical capital will grow in time exactly at the same exogenous rate γ. Also profits will grow at this constant rate, implying that the profit per capital unit is also a constant value in time.

The only change that is proposed to the described scenario consists on the introduction of a different production function; nevertheless, the basic properties of the model should not suffer relevant changes. Considering the human capital per physical capital unit variable, $h(t)$, the production function can be rewritten under an intensive form,
$y(t) = A.\left[a + (1-a).h(t)^{\psi}\right]^{1/\psi}$, with $y(t)$ the output per unit of physical capital.

The   new   profit   expression   will   be

$$\pi(t) \equiv A.\left[a + (1-a).h(t)^{\psi}\right]^{1/\psi} - \gamma - \delta_k - i_h(t).h(t),$$ while constraint (4.8) continues to be a restriction of the problem. The determination of optimality conditions leads to the dynamic equation of the human capital shadow-price, which assumes the following shape,

$$\dot{p}_h(t) = \left[\rho + \delta_h + \gamma - i_h(t)\right]p_h(t) - (1-a).A.\left[a/h(t) + 1 - a\right]^{(1-\psi)/\psi} + i_h(t)$$

The optimality condition (4.13) according to which the shadow-price of human capital is equal to one, allows transforming the above equation into a constant value in time. The outcome is:

$$h(t) = \frac{a}{\left[\dfrac{\rho + \delta_h + \gamma}{(1-a).A}\right]^{\psi/(1-\psi)} - (1-a)}$$

This result should be compared with (4.16). The differences are not too significant. The variable continues to present a constant value that will be as much higher as the better is the technology level and the lower is the value of any of the following parameters: the discount rate, the human capital depreciation rate and the growth rate of the stock of physical capital.

The relative level of investment in human capital, $i_h(t)$, does not suffer any change relatively to the original version of the model; this occurs because according to (4.8), a constant value of the human capital – physical capital ratio implies that the investment in human capital will be, at every time moment, the sum of the growth rate γ with the depreciation rate of human capital.

Finally, the profit expression will be

$$\pi(t) \equiv A.\left[a + (1-a).\left(\frac{a}{\left[\dfrac{\rho + \delta_h + \gamma}{(1-a).A}\right]^{\psi/(1-\psi)} - (1-a)}\right)^{\psi}\right]^{1/\psi}$$
$$- \gamma - \delta_k - \frac{a.(\delta_h + \gamma)}{\left[\dfrac{\rho + \delta_h + \gamma}{(1-a).A}\right]^{\psi/(1-\psi)} - (1-a)}$$

Again, the similarity relatively to the model developed for a Cobb-Douglas production function is evident; the profit is constant in time and dependent on two types of parameters: the various rates that the optimization problem considers and the parameters of the production function.

Application 2

Assume the problem of a firm that invests in communication but where the investment in physical capital is exogenous (section 4.2). For this problem assume the following vector of parameters: $[A \ \mu \ \varepsilon \ \rho \ \gamma \ \delta_h \ \delta_o]$=[0.1 0.8 0.5 0.025 0.05 0.01 0.01].

a) Present the dynamic system underlying the model, assuming as endogenous variables the quantities of human capital and of organizational capital per unit of physical capital;

b) Confirm the existence of a saddle-path equilibrium for the system under consideration. Present the analytical expression of the stable trajectory;

c) Transform the system in question a) of the exercise into a system where the endogenous variables are the stock of human capital (per unit of physical capital) and the investment in human capital (per unit of human capital);

d) For the system in question c) study the impact over the endogenous variables of the perturbation $\Delta^+ \gamma$.

A. Present the Dynamic System Underlying the Model

The required dynamic system is the one composed by Equations (4.33) and (4.34). We recall that this system is obtained from the profit maximization problem of a given firm, when the growth rate of physical capital is exogenous and the investment in communication is aimed at the accumulation of organizational capital, which in turn is an important element for the productivity of the investment in human capital (the larger is the level of organizational capital per unit of physical capital, the larger will be the quantity of human capital that is accumulated per unit of investment in this form of capital).

By simple substitution of parameter values by the values considered in the exercise, one can present the system; we will have

$$\dot{h}(t) = 0.17.o(t)^{1.5} - 0.06.h(t) \ ;$$
$$\dot{o}(t) = 0.16.h(t)^{-0.2}.o(t)^{1.5} - 0.17.o(t)$$

B. Confirm the Existence of a Saddle-Path Equilibrium and Present the Analytical Expression of the Stable Trajectory

With the study of the model in its generic form, in section 4.3, one has derived a relation between parameter values that once obeyed allowed for the existence of a saddle-path equilibrium. This condition, (4.41), is satisfied in the present example, since ε=0.5>(1-0.8)/0.8.

Relatively to the expression of the stable trajectory, this was equally determined in its generic form, corresponding in the case to Equation (4.42). Let us follow the procedure needed to arrive to this equation for the parameter values of the exercise. First, let us quantify the equilibrium values. By solving system $\left[\dot{h}(t), \dot{o}(t)\right] = (0,0)$, one finds the steady-state values $\bar{h} = 21.241$ and $\bar{o} = 3.836$. Also the steady-state values for the investment variables are presentable [these are given in (4.36)]: $\bar{i}_h = 0.031$; $\bar{i}_o = 0.06$. The capital variables are accumulated stocks; the investment variables are flows that at each time moment add to the accumulated values; this is the reason why the first are much higher than the second values, in a steady-state position.

The linearization of the system in the vicinity of the steady-state produces the Jacobian matrix $J = \begin{bmatrix} -0.06 & 0.499 \\ -0.006 & 0.085 \end{bmatrix}$. To matrix J are associated the following eigenvalues: $\lambda_1 =$ -0.035 and $\lambda_2 = 0.06$. To the negative eigenvalue, in turn, it will be associated the eigenvector $P_1 = [20\ 1]$. The slope of the stable trajectory will be the inverse of the first element of the vector, i.e., 0.05. This value confirms the generic results, according to which the saddle-trajectory will have a positive slope (even though this slope will be small). Given the equilibrium values, the saddle-trajectory one is searching for will correspond to the following equation:

$$o(t) = 2.774 + 0.05.h(t).$$

C. Transform the System in A

The profit maximization model with investment in organizational capital was analyzed considering as endogenous the two capital variables, which are two state variables of the problem. The absence of control variables has prevented a richer analysis, namely with regard to the perception of the impact of exogenous perturbations over the equilibrium values. Now, we re-consider the same model, but taking as endogenous variables the stock of human capital and the investment in human capital.

Expression (4.31) establishes an optimal relation between the level of investment in human capital and the capital variables. For the concrete values of the exercise, one will have $i_h(t) = 0.17.\dfrac{o(t)}{h(t)}$. Differentiating this last expression with respect to time, the following relation between growth rates holds, $\dfrac{\dot{i}_h(t)}{i_h(t)} = \dfrac{\dot{o}(t)}{o(t)} - \dfrac{\dot{h}(t)}{h(t)}$. One can use the dynamic equations one has found in item a) of the exercise to write a dynamic equation relating to the variable investment in human capital; one observes that

$$\dot{i}_h(t) = \left[0.388.h(t)^{0.3}.i_h(t)^{0.5} - 2.426.h(t)^{0.5}.i_h(t)^{1.5} - 0.11\right]i_h(t)$$

The equation respecting to the amount of human capital per unit of physical capital can also be presented after the elimination of the organizational capital variable from the expression,

$$\dot{h}(t) = 2.426.h(t)^{1.5}.i_h(t)^{1.5} - 0.06.h(t).$$

With these two last presented equations, we have a new system capable of explaining the motion in time followed jointly by variables human capital and investment in human capital. Since the system that was established respects to the same model as before, the steady-state values are the same as the ones computed in point b) of the exercise, i.e., $\bar{h} = 21.241$ and $\bar{i}_h = 0.031$.

To continue with the dynamic analysis, one linearizes the system in the vicinity of the steady-state, allowing obtaining

$$\begin{bmatrix} \dot{h}(t) \\ \dot{i}_h(t) \end{bmatrix} = \begin{bmatrix} 0.031 & 62.723 \\ 2\times10^{-5} & -0.006 \end{bmatrix} \cdot \begin{bmatrix} h(t) - \bar{h} \\ i_h(t) - \bar{i}_h \end{bmatrix}$$

Note that the trace of the Jacobian matrix corresponds, once again, to the discount rate of future profits, ρ=0.025, while the determinant is a negative value: $Det(J)$=-1.44×10^{-3}. The saddle-path equilibrium that one has found when analyzing the model with the pair of capital variables is confirmed in this version of the problem. To understand the relation between accumulated human capital and investment in human capital, let us draw a phase diagram. The corresponding isoclines are:

$$\dot{h}(t) = 0 \Rightarrow i_h(t) = 0.041 - 4.94 \times 10^{-4}.h(t)$$
$$\dot{i}_h(t) = 0 \Rightarrow i_h(t) = -0.04 + 3.33 \times 10^{-3}.h(t)$$

One of the isoclines has a negative slope and the other one is positively sloped. The elements of the first column of the Jacobian matrix of the linearized system, being both positive values, furnish the following information:

- to the right of $\dot{h}(t) = 0$, one can display horizontal directional arrows pointing to the right;
- to the left of $\dot{h}(t) = 0$, one can present horizontal directional arrows pointing to the left;
- to the right of $\dot{i}_h(t) = 0$, one can present vertical directional arrows pointing up;
- to the left of $\dot{i}_h(t) = 0$, one can display vertical directional arrows pointing down.

The phase diagram is presentable as follows:

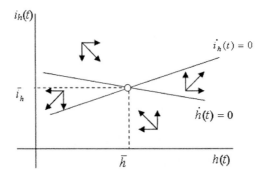

The phase diagram reveals that the stable trajectory will have a negative and relatively large slope. The negative slope indicates that in the eventual situation of convergence towards the steady-state the quantity of human capital and the investment in human capital will have to follow opposite directions; this is only possible because it exists another variable that implicitly determines the dynamics of the model, which is the organizational capital: to obtain better results at the level of accumulation of human capital it is rewardful to divert resources from the direct investment in this form of capital towards communication, since communication stimulates the growth of human capital; human capital does not grow exclusively as the result of the direct investment in this form of capital but also as the result of the organizational capital that is possible to accumulate.

The graphical result can be confirmed analytically. The eigenvalues of the Jacobian matrix are $\lambda_1 = -2.746 \times 10^{-2}$ and $\lambda_2 = 5.246 \times 10^{-2}$. To the negative eigenvalue is associated the eigenvector $P_1=[-1073\ 1]$. The stable trajectory has a negative slope, as one has observed through the graphical representation, and one can present it as

$$i_h(t) - \bar{i}_h = -\frac{1}{1073}.\left[h(t) - \bar{h}\right].$$

D. Study the Impact

The previous analysis relates a state variable, the human capital stock, and a control variable, corresponding this to the investment in the referred form of capital. In this case, it is possible to study the effect of exogenous perturbations having in consideration that it is possible to separate a short-run effect and a long-run effect of the perturbation over the initially observed steady-state.

In this exercise, it is asked to quantify the effect of a positive change in the growth rate of the stock of physical capital. This quantification requires the determination of the corresponding perturbation vector, what implies the need to present the generic form of the equations of the dynamic system (previously, one has just presented the numerical version relating the considered example). The following dynamic equations are found,

$$\dot{h}(t) = \left(\frac{\rho + \delta_o + \gamma}{\varepsilon}\right)^{2+\varepsilon} .h(t)^{1+\varepsilon}.i_h(t)^{1+\varepsilon} - (\delta_h + \gamma).h(t)$$

$$\dot{i}_h(t) =$$

$$\left[\left(\frac{\rho + \delta_o + \gamma}{\varepsilon}\right)^{1+\varepsilon} .h(t)^{\varepsilon}.i_h(t)^{\varepsilon}.\left(\frac{\mu}{\varepsilon}.A.h(t)^{-(1-\mu)}\right) - \frac{\rho}{\varepsilon} - \frac{1-\varepsilon}{\varepsilon}.(\delta_h + \gamma)\right].i_h(t)$$

The disturbances vector will be:

$$J(\gamma) = \begin{bmatrix} \dfrac{\partial \dot{h}(t)}{\partial \gamma(t)} \Big|_{(\bar{h},\bar{i}_h)} \\ \dfrac{\partial \dot{i}_h(t)}{\partial \gamma(t)} \Big|_{(\bar{h},\bar{i}_h)} \end{bmatrix} = \begin{bmatrix} \left[\dfrac{(2+\varepsilon).(\delta_h+\gamma)}{\rho+\delta_o+\gamma} -1 \right]\bar{h} \\ \left[\dfrac{(1+\varepsilon).\left[\dfrac{\rho}{\varepsilon} + \dfrac{1-\varepsilon}{\varepsilon}.(\delta_h+\gamma) \right]}{\rho+\delta_o+\gamma} - \dfrac{1-\varepsilon}{\varepsilon} \right]\bar{i}_h \end{bmatrix}$$

The above vector will be reduced to the following couple of values for the example under analysis: $J(\gamma) = \begin{bmatrix} 16.243 \\ 0.029 \end{bmatrix}$.

The long-run effect over the steady-state [$\bar{h} = 21.241$; $\bar{i}_h = 0.031$] will correspond to

$$\begin{bmatrix} \Delta\bar{h}_\infty \\ \Delta\bar{i}_{h,\infty} \end{bmatrix} = -J^{-1}.J(\gamma).\Delta^+\gamma = \begin{bmatrix} -1,330.4 \\ 0.399 \end{bmatrix}.\Delta^+\gamma.$$

The short-run impact over the control variable corresponds to $\Delta\bar{i}_{h,0} = \Delta\bar{i}_{h,\infty} - \dfrac{p_{21}}{p_{11}}.\Delta\bar{h}_\infty$, i.e., $\Delta\bar{i}_{h,0} = -0.841.\Delta^+\gamma$.

The change in the value of the growth rate of physical capital will disturb the steady-state in the following way: there is an initial jump towards a new stable trajectory that will be located to the left and below the initial one. Once the new stable trajectory is reached there is a convergence of both variables in the direction of the equilibrium point, with this convergence implying an increase on the value of the investment variable and a large fall in the value of the capital variable.

Consider a specific value for the perturbation; let $\Delta^+\gamma=0.01$. In this case, the long-run effects will be: $\begin{bmatrix} \Delta\bar{h}_\infty \\ \Delta\bar{i}_{h,\infty} \end{bmatrix} = \begin{bmatrix} -13.304 \\ 0.00399 \end{bmatrix}$, and the short-run impact over the investment variable is $\Delta\bar{i}_{h,0} = -0.00841$. Thus, at the moment in which the change in the value of the physical capital growth rate occurs, the steady-state point is abandoned in favour of point $\bar{h} = 21.241$; $\bar{i}_h = 0.02259$. From this point forward, there is convergence to the new equilibrium, which corresponds to $\bar{h} = 7.937$; $\bar{i}_h = 0.03499$.

Regarding the interpretation of the movements described above, one can say that the growth of the stock of physical capital implies an increase in the investment in human capital, but the stock of human capital per unit of physical capital will be lower in the long-run, what essentially implies a replacement of human capital by physical capital in production.

The impact of the perturbation is graphically sketched in the figure that follows.

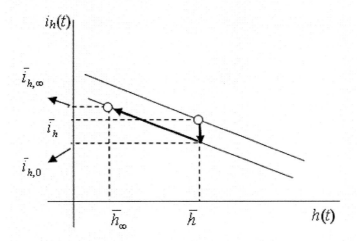

Application 3

Recover the parameter vector of the previous application and add to it a depreciation rate for physical capital: $\delta_k=0.005$. For the model one has considered in section 4.4, where physical capital emerges as an endogenous variable, determine the values of equilibrium and discuss the stability of this equilibrium.

By adding physical capital accumulation decisions to the decisions of investment in human and organizational capital, the model has gained a state variable (the stock of physical capital) and a control variable (investment in physical capital) that one has to add to the already assumed pairs of capital variables and investment variables.

Throughout section 4.4 one has understood that the introduction of new variables has not increased the dimension of the model's dynamics. On the contrary, one has observed that the time motion described by the model could be synthesized in a single differential equation relating to the organizational capital variable per unit of physical capital. This Equation, (4.64), takes the following shape for the assumed array of parameter values:

$$\dot{o}(t) = \left\{ 0.06.\left[0.03 + 0.035.o(t) \right]^{-0.25}.o(t)^{0.5} - 0.07 \right\}.o(t)$$

For this equation there is a unique steady-state point: $\overline{o} = 0.27$. Having determined the steady-state value for the organizational capital quantity per unit of physical capital, one may resort to (4.63) to obtain the equilibrium value of the variable human capital (also per unit of physical capital): $\overline{h} = 1.145$. From condition (4.59) is also possible to withdraw the equilibrium value of the investment in human capital (by unit of human capital):

$$\overline{i}_h = \frac{\rho + \delta_o}{\varepsilon}.\frac{\overline{o}}{\overline{h}} = 0.016.$$ Finally, expression (4.61) is equivalent, in the steady-state, to the

following difference between investment values, $\overline{i}_o - \overline{i}_k = 0.016$. One concludes, with this last result, that the investment in organizational capital is a larger value relatively to the investment in physical capital in an amount identical to the investment that was made in human capital. Note that the investment variables are defined in units of already accumulated capital and that the equilibrium results are valid under a scenario of optimization of the investment decisions by the firm.

Relatively to the analysis of stability one can follow one of two ways: we can draw the differential equation concerning the accumulation of organizational capital and evaluate the dynamics graphically, or, alternatively, one may linearize the equation in the vicinity of the steady-state, with the found slope allowing to determine if the equilibrium is stable (negative slope) or unstable (positive slope).

The linearization of the equation allows finding the following derivative: $\left. \dfrac{\partial \dot{o}(t)}{\partial o(t)} \right|_{\bar{o}} \approx 0.035$. Since this value is positive, the steady-state is unstable. The equilibrium result will not be attained. The obtained value is the slope of the differential equation when linearized in the vicinity of the steady-state; such linearization yields $\dot{o}(t) = 0.035.[o(t) - \bar{o}]$.

To confirm the instability result, we draw the corresponding phase diagram; one observes that the value of the organizational capital stock falls to the left of the steady-state point and rises to its right. This means that any initial point that does not coincide with the steady-state will imply a progressive departure relatively to such equilibrium point.

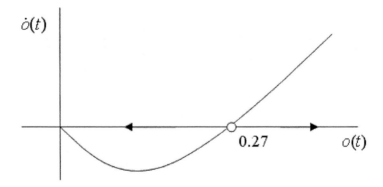

The figure reinforces the conclusion that for an initial level of organizational capital below the equilibrium one there will be, for the set of values of parameters one has chosen to adopt, a tendency for the investment in communication to vanish, what leads us back to the initial model in which we only had investment in human capital and in physical capital as instruments to optimize the behavior of the firm given the goal of profit maximization.

Chapter 5

COMMUNICATION AND ECONOMICS: THE DIGITAL GOODS[*]

In this last chapter, we intend to discuss how the development of the capacity and of the instruments to communicate generates a new economic reality. In chapter 1, we have highlighted that communication is changing. The rise of new media, in the context of the new technologies, allows re-thinking communication. Communication will maintain its basic structure as a dynamic interaction process among human beings, but it makes a progressively larger use of complex channels that allow to further explore the potentialities of creating new ways of contact and interaction. Individuals have today, at their disposal, multiple forms of interaction in order to attain multiple possible goals.

In order to identify how the new media allow for new interaction realities, this last chapter concentrates on the economic system. Without abandoning the dynamic setting, one intends to go beyond the communication process, to explain how the evolution of the communication skills has allowed gaining new insights on how to develop the economic activity. One of the aims of the analysis consists in discussing how a special kind of economic goods, that by their nature are intrinsic to the communication process, are produced and traded; we are referring to the digital goods.

One of the fundamental characteristics of the economic system is change. The produced goods, the means of transaction and the consumer preferences tend to change over time. Certainly the decisions of a consumer in any developed country are today much different from the decisions that any individual has taken 500 years ago in order to maximize her utility. This occurs because the variety and the quantity available to the agent are much different, because the ways to access markets have changed and because the structure of the labor market has changed with implications in the amount and in the type of income one obtains. Likewise, a given firm faces in the contemporaneous world other types of challenges and opportunities that did not exist in the past. Nevertheless, the essence of the economic problems of consumers and producers has not been modified even though there are obvious differences in terms of complexity and scale.

As always, the decision problem of the consumer continues to be consumption utility maximization given some budget constraint that limits her choices and the problem of the

---

[*] This last chapter develops, in a more detailed way, the ideas presented in Gomes (2004).

producer consists, now as in the past, in managing revenues and costs in order to maximize profits. In reality, the dimension of the economic system has changed, but its nature remains the same. The reason for the unchangeable nature of the economic problems is founded on the evidence that the most significant part of the goods traded today is not significantly different from the type of goods exchanged in the past. The cloths, the transportation vehicles, the food and other goods may be produced today under more sophisticated techniques, however their basic economic properties remain the same as before. The most relevant of these properties is rivalry: the use of a good by an individual turns it impossible for the same unit of the good to be used simultaneously by another individual.

The recent evolution of the economic system leads to the recognition that more than the simple scale and frequency of the economic transactions is changing. There is an immaterial component of the transactions, attached to a particular type of goods and services with distinctive characteristics relatively to the trivial private goods, that is gaining a decisive weight in economic trade. The digital goods or knowledge goods have been introducing, throughout the last few years, an immaterial side into the economic activity that is evidenced at multiple levels: in trade and therefore in the organization and structure of markets, in production, in the techniques used to gain efficiency, in innovation (from new forms of management to the introduction of new varieties of goods and services or sophistication of the existing ones), and even at the level of consumption, essentially in what relates changes on the typical basket of goods and services that consumers purchase; this basket includes progressively more goods with the characteristics of this new immaterial or intangible reality.

It is undeniable the emergence and strengthening of an economy of knowledge, where the immaterial activities gain weight and where the knowledge-driven component is essential, as discussed in Murteira, Nicolau, Mendes and Martins (2001). However it is not so straightforward to understand what the knowledge economy and the goods that it trades mean in terms of the configuration of a new economy and how one can attach to it a new form of facing and thinking reality; the central question relates with the evaluation of what is truly new in order to understand if a different theoretical paradigm is required for the understanding of the new phenomena, or if, on the contrary, the existing theory is sufficiently rich and flexible to continue to give credible explanations about the way agents produce, trade and consume.

For a better understanding of the relevance of intangibility let us address separately each one of the three fundamental questions of the economic system:

a) Production. From the productive point of view, the knowledge goods can be associated to the technological revolution that the new information and communication technologies (ICT) have introduced. The progress achieved at the efficiency and productivity level can be remarked as quantitatively more significant than the progress allowed by previous technological revolutions; however, as Quah (2001) highlights, from a qualitative point of view there is in this revolution nothing radically new; one can easily establish a parallel between this and other great technological mutations of the past, meaning that the ICT can be interpreted at the same level of what the invention of the wheel or the set of inventions that allowed for the first phase of the industrial revolution have brought in terms of shaping the economic organization we have today;

b) Consumption. The emergence of the new economy, intangible economy or *weightless economy*, as designated by Quah (1998), innovates relatively to other moments of evolution in the economic system precisely because it is not restricted to being reflected in an additional fast and substantial increment on productivity. On the demand side another revolution is occurring. The knowledge goods are much more than simple productive inputs; in fact, as inputs they are not anything substantially new, because knowledge has always been used as productive input, both the available scientific knowledge and the human knowledge acquired from learning and practicing. The knowledge goods are today more than ever a relevant part of the consumption of a large majority of households, i.e., if until recently in our history individuals typically consumed material goods containing knowledge, now progressively more the knowledge itself is consumed as a final good. Some examples at this level have become trivial: today we consume videogames, computer software, digital pictures and music, telecommunication services and access to internet contents in the same way that we acquire material goods that have always been present in our basket of consumption, as it is the case of food and clothes.

The clear distinction between what really are knowledge goods and material or private goods will be addressed later in this introduction; for now, the essential point consists in understanding that there is, in fact, a substantial change in the structure of consumption. Human knowledge, which has always been seen as a key input in the generation of wealth, a theme that was the subject of influential studies by some of the most prominent economists of the twentieth century, as Schultz (1961) and Becker (1964), must now be, in order to adjust the interpretation of reality to a changing environment, incorporated into the utility function representing the consumption preferences of individuals.

c) Transactions. A third sphere where the weightless economy should be addressed is the one relating the transference of property from the ones that produce to the ones that consume. In reality, the new economy has not only contributed to increase productive efficiency or to introduce a revolution in the structure of consumption profiles; it also served, and this may be the most evident change, for the emergence of new forms of organizing markets, i.e., it allowed for new ways of trading goods and services. At this level, it is important to understand what changed at the level of the efficiency in transactions, i.e., if the information gains that were achieved and that are still to be achieved in the future are relevant and compensate eventual obstacles that the new economy is likely to produce at the level of competition and market efficiency.

The weightless economy will not be associated only to the ICT and to the internet, but this is surely one of its most visible elements. The internet is the communication instrument of faster growth ever and it is much more than a unilateral mean of communication, as opposed to most of the traditional communication means; the internet may be conceived as a market in the sense that it works as an integrated system of communication where producers and consumers can interact.

One can argue that the internet brings nothing new to the way in which markets work; it is just one additional system for the exchange of information that helps in the trading activity but that does not differ substantially relatively to other forms of accessing information. Nevertheless, there are no other means with such a global pervasiveness and such low costs in the dissemination of information and contact between economic agents as the internet, which in fact as provided at this level outstanding changes.

By interpreting internet as a market, it is convenient to address the characteristics implying a more or less competitive or a more or less concentrated market structure. Although the remarkable gains in terms of information that the ICT allow for, which are a fundamental piece in allowing the markets to approach a perfectly competitive environment, one cannot forget the other side of the story: by providing global markets, the internet stimulates concentration and the survival of the ones who have already a relatively large dimension.

This is another fundamental characteristic of the new economy, which given the increasing dimension and the kind of activities and means that it involves promotes scale economies and therefore concentrated markets where a small number of firms dominate. Concentration implies, normally, a lower efficiency given that the properties of openness (free entry and exit of firms in the market) and atomicity (the incapacity of the firms given their small dimension to assume a different role other than price takers) are lost, implying relevant damages for the consumer and the competitors with a small dimension.

Several empirical studies, as Freund and Weinhold (2002) and Brown and Goolsbee (2002) among others, emphasize the information gains that the internet allows for, even though most of the time transactions are not made through it (to a large share of the consumers the internet will work as a kind of yellow pages where data is searched in order to form purchasing decisions, and not as a supermarket where one does not only compare prices but also undertakes, simultaneously, the transaction).

Other studies, as the one by Smith, Bailey and Brynjolfsson (2000), point to the perverse effects that the internet may lead to. It can represent a way to discriminate prices through product differentiation and it involves problems of asymmetric information, in the sense that the ones who place information in the internet have the ability to control and manipulate such information, i.e., many times internet cannot escape being a simple advertising vehicle that transmits to the consumer only what the firm finds convenient to be revealed, given its own interests.

At this level, the ICT are particularly relevant for the goods of the new economy; if these goods are essentially digital goods they can be evaluated without the need of physical presence without losing relevant information about what they effectively are; however, for the goods of the traditional economy, the evaluation of their properties through the simple description of the characteristics through a multimedia communication channel makes it hard to achieve successful transactions, because at every transaction process there are conflicting interests between buyer and seller that introduce information asymmetry problems, which are increased by physical distance.

The previous remarks furnish the following relevant ideas about what the new economy effectively is: it is a set of technical achievements and new goods that emerged at a given point in time allowing for productivity gains, for new forms of perceiving consumption utility, and for markets with an increased efficiency potential but that simultaneously are easier to manipulate by the agents with more weight in the market. Some authors, as Goldhaber (1997), Aigrain (1997) and Ghosh (1998) go even further and launch the discussion on how the economic science should change its main paradigms given a reality that is completely different from the one previous to the internet era. One of the curious aspects raised by this group of authors relates to the argument that internet allows to withdraw relevance to money in the way the economy works.

Examples as the ones provided by many types of open source software [Browne (1998)] can represent the emergence of a new kind of economic organization, where all contribute with the knowledge good in order for this to be available to all. At this level what is a supply process is simultaneously a demand process: the ones offering their knowledge on the net search for recognition, and in this sense this market will not be different from any other because there is a demand, a supply and an equilibrium. The decisive point is that the equilibrium will not correspond to a situation where a good is traded for an amount of money but a situation where knowledge is traded by recognition.

It is not the purpose of this text to discuss in detail the transformations in the economic system of the referred new phenomena, but one should address these issues with the attention they deserve: can the internet help in configuring an economic system where a part of the transactions, by their nature and by the nature of the goods they involve, escape the logic of economic organization that is nowadays dominant?

The objective of this text is far from having the ambition of explaining the way in which the *weightless economy* introduces changes in the way the economic system works. Choosing a more conventional and less radical approach one intends, in this chapter, to integrate the knowledge goods into a modelling structure close the one of the traditional economic analysis. Our basic problem will be a problem of consumption utility maximization that some representative agent faces given her budget constraint. For this analysis to be successful, one first needs to rigorously define what the new economy goods are. Here, we follow Quah (2002).

For Quah (2002) the distinctive goods of the *weightless economy* can be designated by digital goods and they are generically defined as sequences of zeros and ones with economic value (or bitstrings). The digital goods will correspond, then, to everything that can be encoded and sent from one place to another without the need of a physical transfer.[2] The digital goods are the ones we are used to store in our personal computer and to send to others through the internet, being these chemical formulae, DNA sequences, mathematical theorems, digital music and images, software with work or entertainment purposes. One should be careful not to make confusion between the digital good and its physical support. Many digital goods are traded associated with a physical support; for instance a compact disk is a physical object and therefore it can be analyzed in terms of economic significance as any private good. However, the music that it contains is a digital good with specific properties.

The following five properties are the ones identified by Quah (2002) in order to define digital goods:

1) Non rivalry. The private goods, the ones that are commonly traded in the market, are rival, i.e., the respective consumption eliminates the existence of the good. The digital goods, in turn, can be consumed by an agent without this meaning the disappearance of the good; it will remain available in the same form for another agent to consume or for the same agent to consume it again in a posterior moment of

---

[2] Scientific fiction has already, for a long-time, trasformed the human being in a bitstring. The teletransportation machine of the Startrek series allowed for such a possibility. In reality, physical goods and living beings do not

time. The non rivalry property is not an exclusive property of the digital goods; any public or semi-public good assumes this property, as the national defence, the police or the supply of electricity. But in our discussion it is mainly relevant that it is a property of every digital good: for instance, the access of someone to a videogame does not damage the possibility of this being consumed by others in a posterior time moment.

2) Infinite expansibility. Digital goods, as other goods, have associated production costs; however, differently from a large part of the other goods they do not have expansability costs. After the first unit of the good is produced, the available quantity can be arbitrarily increased without incurring in additional costs and in an almost instantaneous way. In a game for *Playstation* or for *X-Box* the cost concentrates in conceiving the first unit; for the following ones, the reproduction is immediate and at almost no cost.

This property has major implications over the functioning and structure of markets. First, because the costs associated to the production of the first unit are typically very high, what implies that the markets for digital goods are characterized by a strong concentration on the supply side; i.e., they are industries where increasing returns to scale prevail and therefore a restrict number of producers can exist. Secondly, these markets only survive if there is some kind of exclusion mechanism relatively to non authorized reproduction; the clear definition of intellectual property rights is a central element for the economy of the digital goods to succeed, what is evident from the fact of having the production costs concentrated on the generated of the first unit of the good.

3) Discretion. Associated to the idea of infinite expansibility is the concept of discretion, which tells us that relatively to the digital goods it only matters, from the point of view of consumption or use of the good, entire units of the good. Particularly it will matter an entire unit (since from this, the reproduction for other units is immediate). Less than a unit has no utility: we can find no use for half an idea, half of the information needed to run some computer program, half of a genetic code or half the scenes of a movie. Differently from what happens for private goods (e.g., consuming a part of an orange allows to withdraw the corresponding level of utility), no utility is withdrawn from possessing only a share of the digital good.

4) A-spatiality. It is not completely correct to say that once produced a digital good is available in every possible location. Nevertheless, the digital goods can be considered a-spatial in the sense that they disrespect the physical distance. Practically at the same time and with the same cost the digital good can be disseminated at short or at long distances. This property collides, in an obvious way, with what one is used to observe for the commonly considered economic goods. Thus, it may be necessary to review location and trade theories (namely international trade) at the light of this new reality. The question of a-spatiality is one of the most relevant questions regarding the economics of digital goods; nevertheless, this will be the less explored issue in this chapter, since we will be mainly concerned with intertemporal aspects and neglect issues concerning the location of economic activities.

---

possess this property; however, an increasing share of production inputs, intermediate goods and final goods can effectively be 'teletransported'.

5) Recombination. The digital goods can be recombined. This essentially means that the information needed to produce a good can easily be converted in order to give birth to another digital good (for instance, the information contained in a newspaper article can be used to produce a television program).[3]

The previous five properties would allow formulating several models where the distinction between the economy of the non digital goods and the economy of the digital goods could be confronted. This is basically the way one follows in the subsequent sections, with particular emphasis on how consumption utility is disturbed by the consideration of digital goods. One of the fundamental points to highlight is that the idea of bitstring (sequence of zeros and ones) has a two-fold meaning: it respects to the physical characteristics of the digital goods, as mentioned, but also to the way in which these goods can be modelled from an economic theory point of view.

The contents of this chapter will be inspired in two points largely referred in this introduction, First: the digital goods possess characteristics that clearly separate them from the goods typically addressed by the economic theory; Second: the economy we live in today is in an increasing percentage an economy of digital goods.

The contents of the chapter are summarized in what follows. Section 5.1 approaches consumption preferences, revealing distinct indifference maps for digital goods and non digital goods. The fundamental message is that to the bitstrings is not associated the property of convex preferences which is one of the fundamental axioms of the utility theory according with the formulation of Arrow and Debreu (1954). Non convexities do not imply, however, that the utility maximization problem cannot be addressed with the simultaneous consideration of digital and non digital goods. As in the majority of the economic problems, the combination of a budget constraint with a given representation of preferences through a utility function will allow for a choice, of the representative consumer, of the amounts of digital and non digital goods to acquire. This problem is presented in section 5.2.

The utility maximization problem can be sophisticated through the introduction of a dynamic constraint regarding the accumulation of capital. In section 5.3, the digital goods are integrated in a problem of optimal control, together with a homogeneous private good. This structure will allow for finding a time trajectory of consumption in which it is possible to determine with accuracy the time moment in which one should begin acquiring or one should not acquire any more a given digital good given the basket of digital and non digital goods already acquired by the consumer.

The analysis of sections 5.1 to 5.3 interprets the digital goods essentially in a perspective of demand / consumption, i.e., the analysis is silent in what concerns the production of any kind of the two types of goods. Since, according to what one has discussed, the production process of digital goods has specific properties (namely at the level of infinite expansibility and recombination) section 5.4 provides an analytical structure where one can distinguish between the production of the two types of goods. The sector that produces digital goods will produce having as a reference past productive results (given the property of recombination)

---

[3] Relatively to the newspaper article this is a good example of the distinction between the digital good and the corresponding physical support. The article is a digital good, possessing the five mentioned properties. The paper in which it is printed will be a private good, exhibiting the rivalry and excludability that we know these possess.

and only the production of the first unit will matter, since the assumed goods are infinitely expansible.

Section 5.5 addresses some applications.

5.1. PREFERENCES AND NON CONVEXITY

The theory of utility for private goods is a central piece of the economic science. With the work of Arrow and Debreu (1954) the way in which consumers face the process of consumption choices based on their own preferences can be synthesized in a small set of axioms that support the analytical treatment of the problem of the representative consumer. Let $x^i=(x_1, ..., x_n)$ be some vector of private goods (or non digital goods), with x_i, $i=1, ...,$ n, the quantity of each good that the assumed basket contains. Consider as well the following preference relations, $\succsim$ and $\precsim$, which indicate, respectively, that a given basket x^i is at least as preferable as and not as preferred as a second basket x^j, and $\geq$ and $>=$ are operators meaning, respectively, that a first basket includes at least as much quantity of goods as another basket and that the first basket contains a larger quantity of goods than the second. The following five axioms constitute the fundamental structure of the economic theory of utility.[4]

Axiom 1 (complete set): $\forall\ x^1, x^2 \in R^n_+, x^1 \succsim x^2$ or $x^2 \succsim x^1$.

Axiom 2 (transitivity): $\forall\ x^1, x^2, x^3 \in R^n_+, x^1 \succsim x^2$ and $x^2 \succsim x^3 \Rightarrow x^1 \succsim x^3$.

Axiom 3 (continuity): $\forall\ x \in R^n_+, \succsim (x)$ and $\precsim (x)$ are closed sets in R^n_+. (the represented sets are, respectively, the set of baskets of goods at least as preferred as x and the set of baskets of goods not preferable to x).

Axiom 4 (strict monotonicity): $\forall\ x^1, x^2 \in R^n_+$, if $x^1 \geq x^2$ then $x^1 \succsim x^2$. If $x^1 >= x^2$ then $x^1 \succ x^2$ (with $\succ$ a preference relation indicating that the first basket is strictly preferred relatively to the second one).

Axiom 5 (convexity): if $x^1 \succ x^2$ then $t.x^1+(1-t).x^2 \succsim x^2$, $\forall t \in [0,1]$.

Are these axioms applicable to digital goods? To discuss this point two of the properties of the digital goods are especially relevant: discretion and infinite expansibility. With these two properties, one will be able to realize that a basket of digital goods should not be considered for the whole set R^n_+, what implies the absence of convexity of preferences in the presence of digital goods.

---

[4] See Jehle and Reny (2001) for a detailed explanation of the meaning of these axioms.

The discretion property states that the digital goods are only relevant from the point of view of consumption for entire quantities of the good (half of an idea or half of a genetic code do not generate any utility for consumers). On the other hand, infinite expansibility implies that the individual just needs to acquire one unit of the good because the good can be reproduced endlessly and without additional costs. Besides the physical property that allowed to define the digital goods as bitstrings, from the point of view of consumption utility a basket of digital goods is also a sequence of zeros and ones, given that only two possibilities matter in what concerns the possession of the good: the possession of an entire unit of the good or the possession of less than an entire unit. Letting symbol ~ represent an indifference relation between any two quantities, one can establish for a digital good z_i the condition $z_i \in R^n_+$ but: $z_i \sim 0$ if $z_i \in [0,1)$ and $z_i \sim 1$ if $z_i \in [1,+\infty)$.

In what concerns the utility theory one can ignore any quantity of z_i that is different from 0 or 1 and therefore one can consider the set $Z=\{0,1\}$ such that $z_i \in Z$. For n digital goods, one will be interested on the definition of axioms in the set $Z^n \equiv \{(z_1, ..., z_n) | z_i \in Z, i=1, ..., n\}$. In this set, one defines vectors $z \equiv (z_1, ..., z_n)$.

Taking the set Z^n and the vectors defined in it, the first four axioms of preferences presented above continue to hold: the preferences are for the digital goods, as for any others, complete, transitive, continuous and monotonic.

The axiom of convexity will no longer hold. For instance, given two vectors $z^0=(1,0)$ and $z^1=(0,1)$, for which one assumes the relation $z^1 \succ^{\sim} z^0$ it is not true that under any $t \in (0,1)$ the condition $(t,1-t) \succ^{\sim} (0,1)$ will hold because $(t,1-t) \sim (0,0)$, what, given the strict monotonicity axiom, implies denying the referred condition. Thus, in what concerns digital goods, preferences are not convex; the conventional theory of utility fails for the digital goods because one of its supporting axioms is no longer valid.

For private goods, the ordering of preferences allows to represent an indifference map in which a series of convex curves relatively to the origin represents distinct levels of utility. A way to clearly distinguish between digital and non digital goods can consists in representing an indifference map for digital goods. Consider a pair of digital goods, z_1 and z_2, in order to graphically represent the indifference map. Assume the following vectors $z^i \in Z^2$: $z^0=(0,0)$, $z^1=(0,1)$, $z^2=(1,0)$ and $z^3=(1,1)$. Defining the set of vectors that from the point of view of preferences are indifferent in terms of utility relatively to z^i by

$$\sim (z^i) \equiv \{z | z \in Z^2, z \sim z^i\} \qquad (5.1)$$

one can graphically present four indifference spaces, which are represented in figure 5.1.

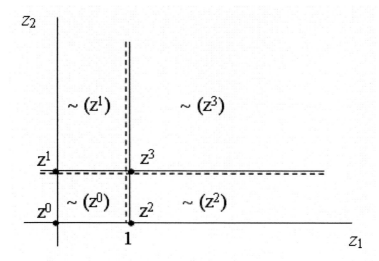

Figure 5.1. Indifference spaces for digital goods.

The indifference spaces in figure 5.1 correspond to the following four sets in $\boldsymbol{R}^2_+$:

$$\sim(\mathbf{z^0})\equiv\{\mathbf{z}|\ 0\leq z_1<1,\ 0\leq z_2<1\} \tag{5.2}$$

$$\sim(\mathbf{z^1})\equiv\{\mathbf{z}|\ 0\leq z_1<1,\ z_2\geq1\} \tag{5.3}$$

$$\sim(\mathbf{z^2})\equiv\{\mathbf{z}|\ z_1\geq1,\ 0\leq z_2<1\} \tag{5.4}$$

$$\sim(\mathbf{z^3})\equiv\{\mathbf{z}|\ z_1\geq1,\ z_2\geq1\} \tag{5.5}$$

In the presence of sets (5.2) to (5.5), and given that the representative consumer will face a budget constraint that leads her, in a rational perspective, to choose baskets of goods with a minimal cost in a same set of indifferent baskets, then from the point of view of the rational consumer only four baskets will matter: $\mathbf{z^0}$, $\mathbf{z^1}$, $\mathbf{z^2}$ and $\mathbf{z^3}$. Given the monotonicity axiom, we know that there is not any basket strictly preferred relatively to $\mathbf{z^3}$ and that any other basket is at least as preferred as $\mathbf{z^0}$.

In the world of private goods it is well known that the maximization of utility is addressable by considering a set of convex indifference curves and a budget constraint that will indicate which is the curve of highest utility level that the budget constraint can touch; the point of contact between the resource constraint and the indifference curve representing the highest achievable level of utility will reveal which is the composition of the optimal basket of goods. In the digital goods world, depending on the location of the budget constraint the agent will consume one unit of both goods, one unit of a single good, or nothing from both digital goods.

Another way of approaching the utility theory in the presence of digital goods consists in assuming a mixed economic system, where digital goods co-exist with non digital goods. In order to represent the indifference map we consider just one type of digital goods (z) e and one type of non digital good (x). For a given level of utility u_0 one can draw an indifference curve as the one presented in figure 5.2.

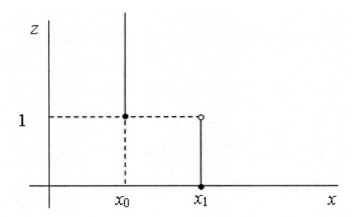

Figure 5.2. Indifference curve representing a given utility level for the relation between a digital good and a non digital good.

The indifference curve in figure 5.2 reveals that for $z<1$ the considered level of utility allows to consume a quantity x_1 of good x, while good z will not be consumed, according to the notion of discretion. For $z\geq1$, the digital good will be consumed and, consequently, given that this will contribute positively for the consumer's utility, to attain the same level of utility it will be necessary to consume a lower quantity of the non digital good: $x_0<x_1$. Any other utility level can be drawn in the exactly same way. For instance, for $u_1>u_0$ we will have two segments of line that are parallel to the ones in figure 5.2; they will be located to the right of the ones in the figure, since they represent a higher utility level.

5.2. UTILITY MAXIMIZATION

The analysis of the previous section can be complemented by introducing the notion of utility function. Consider the following utility function of constant elasticity of substitution (CES) for non digital goods:

$$U(\mathbf{x}) = \left(\int_0^n x_i^\rho . di \right)^{1/\rho}, 0<\rho<1, x_i \in \mathbf{R}. \tag{5.6}$$

Utility function (5.6) considers a continuum of non digital goods in the interval $[0,n]$ and it implicitly takes an ordering of preferences that respects the utility axioms defined along section 5.1. We can consider, without loss of generality, that a part of the goods in function (5.6) are digital goods; for $m\leq n$ digital goods, we re-write (5.6):

$$U(\mathbf{x}, \mathbf{z}) = \left(\int_0^m z_i^\rho . di + \int_m^n x_j^\rho . dj \right)^{1/\rho}, 0<\rho<1, z_i \in \{0,1\}, x_j \in \mathbf{R}. \tag{5.7}$$

Recovering the particular case of a single digital good and a single non digital good, the utility function is reduced to expression (5.8):

$$U(x,z) = \begin{cases} x, & z = 0 \\ \left(x^\rho + 1\right)^{1/\rho}, & z = 1 \end{cases} \qquad (5.8)$$

With the utility function (5.8) and assuming some utility level u_0, one confirms that any indifference curve relating digital and non digital goods will have the shape evidenced in figure 5.2. Note that for $z=0$ we have $x=u_0$, while for $z=1$ it is true that $x = \left(u_0^\rho - 1\right)^{1/\rho}$. Figure 5.2 makes sense for $\left(u_0^\rho - 1\right)^{1/\rho} < u_0$, a condition that effectively has to hold, what is easy to confirm by rearranging the terms and presenting the equivalent expression: $u_0^\rho - 1 < u_0^\rho$.

Assume a budget constraint $y \geq p_x.x + p_z.z$, where y corresponds to the budget endowment of the considered representative agent and p_x and p_z are the prices of goods x and z respectively. With this constraint and utility function (5.8) one can establish an optimization problem that, in fact, can be understood as a pair of problems:

For $z=0$: *Max x* subject to $p_x.x \leq y$;

For $z=1$: *Max* $\left(x^\rho + 1\right)^{1/\rho}$ subject to $p_x.x + p_z.z \leq y$

By solving the optimization problems, one obtains the following optimal results for the consumption of the non digital good: $x^*=y/p_x$ ($z=0$) and $x^*=y/p_x - p_z/p_x$ ($z=1$). These results indicate that the consumed quantity of good x when the digital good is not acquired corresponds to the real value of income, while when good z is purchased, the consumed quantity of good x will be equivalent to the real value of income subtracted by the relative price of the digital good relatively to the private good.

Consider now the existence of two digital goods and of a homogeneous private good x representing all non digital goods and with characteristics of private goods. The following maximization problem is assumed:

$$Max\, U(z_1, z_2, x) = \left(\sum_{i=1}^{2} z_i^\rho + x^\rho \right)^{1/\rho}$$

subject to $y \geq p_1.z_1 + p_2.z_2 + p_x.x$ \hfill (5.9)

Considering that there is a correspondence between the income in the budget constraint and the expenditure of the representative agent, the inequality of constraint (5.9) can be transformed into an equality and therefore good x can be defined as

$$x = \frac{y}{p_x} - \frac{p_1}{p_x}.z_1 - \frac{p_2}{p_x}.z_2 \qquad (5.10)$$

With a constant y and given relative prices, the maximization problem is transformed in a problem without constraints:

$$Max\, U(z_1, z_2) = \left[\sum_{i=1}^{2} z_i^{\,\rho} + \left(\frac{y}{p_x} - \frac{p_1}{p_x}.z_1 - \frac{p_2}{p_x}.z_2 \right)^{\rho} \right]^{1/\rho} \qquad (5.11)$$

For utility function (5.11) only four possibilities are admissible:

$U(0,0) = y/p_x;$

$$U(1,0) = \left[1 + \left(\frac{y}{p_x} - \frac{p_1}{p_x} \right)^{\rho} \right]^{1/\rho} \quad ;$$

$$U(0,1) = \left[1 + \left(\frac{y}{p_x} - \frac{p_2}{p_x} \right)^{\rho} \right]^{1/\rho} \quad ;$$

$$U(1,1) = \left[2 + \left(\frac{y}{p_x} - \frac{p_1 + p_2}{p_x} \right)^{\rho} \right]^{1/\rho}$$

Depending on the values of parameters / exogenous variables ρ, y, p_1, p_2 and p_x, the consumer will choose the option of acquisition of goods that produces the highest level of utility. For each one of the four possibilities one can quantify the acquired quantity of the homogeneous non digital good; this result is obtained directly from the constraint.

in the absence of acquisition of any digital good: $x^* = y/p_x;$

if the optimal result requires the acquisition of digital good z_1 but not the acquisition of z_2: $x^* = y/p_x - p_1/p_x;$

if the optimal result requires the acquisition of digital good z_2 but not the acquisition of z_1: $x^* = y/p_x - p_2/p_x;$

if both digital goods are acquired under optimality: $x^* = y/p_x - (p_1 + p_2)/p_x;$

The previous results are straightforward to generalize for n digital goods; in this case,

$$Max\, U(\mathbf{z}) = \left[\int_0^n z_i^{\,\rho}.di + \left(\frac{y}{p_x} - \int_0^n \frac{p_i}{p_x}.z_i.di \right)^{\rho} \right]^{1/\rho} \qquad (5.12)$$

The maximization techniques for convex preferences cannot be applied to a problem with discrete good as it is the case of (5.12). Here, maximization requires comparing 2^n possible utilities, which correspond to 2^n combinations in terms of acquisition of digital goods. The utility will reach a maximum for some vector z^* to which it corresponds the highest possible value of $U(z)$ in (5.12); this vector of dimension n is composed by zeros and ones and it will be associated to an optimal quantity of the non digital good given by

$$x^* = \frac{y}{p_x} - \int_0^n \frac{p_i}{p_x}.z_i.di,$$ with each variable z_1 assuming only one of the values of the set

$\{0,1\}$.

Consider an example. Let the number of digital goods be 3: z_1, z_2 and z_3, with the corresponding prices being: $p_1=3$, $p_2=2$ and $p_3=4$. A non homogeneous non digital good x costs $p_x=6$. The budget endowment of the consumer is $y=12$ and the parameter of the utility function takes the value $\rho=0.5$. Eight possibilities regarding the acquisition of digital goods are possible; we list these possibilities below, presenting the levels of utility that will be found for the specific functional form of the utility function one has considered in (5.12).

$z=(0,0,0)$: $U(z)=2$;
$z=(1,0,0)$: $U(z)=[1+(1.5)^{0.5}]^2=4.9495$;
$z=(0,1,0)$: $U(z)=[1+(5/3)^{0.5}]^2=5.2487$;
$z=(0,0,1)$: $U(z)=[1+(4/3)^{0.5}]^2=4.6427$;
$z=(1,1,0)$: $U(z)=[2+(7/6)^{0.5}]^2=9.4872$;
$z=(1,0,1)$: $U(z)=[2+(5/6)^{0.5}]^2=8.4848$;
$z=(0,1,1)$: $U(z)=[2+(1)^{0.5}]^2=9$;
$z=(1,1,1)$: $U(z)=[3+(0.5)^{0.5}]^2=13.7426$;

According with the presented results, the best choice for the consumer, the one that maximizes utility, will consist in the purchase of the three digital goods, what implies purchasing the following quantity of the non digital good: $x^*=12/6-(3+2+4)/6=0.5$. By acquiring the three digital goods, the agent will have access to a lower quantity of the non digital good, but in terms of utility it will be the best choice.

The previous analysis has revealed that it is relatively simple to build a scenario in which the digital goods are acquired jointly with a given homogeneous good; thus, digital goods are straightforward to integrate into a rather conventional economic analysis. If this is true for a static scenario as the considered one, it will also be true for the intertemporal approach of consumption utility. In what follows, we will introduce a dynamic constraint into the model in order to perceive how the digital goods can influence the optimal time trajectory of consumption, i.e., the time trajectory that maximizes consumption utility.

5.3. OPTIMAL CONTROL

In order to assume a dynamic or intertemporal scenario, take the following rule for the generation of income in an economy:

$$\dot{k}(t) = A.k(t)^{\alpha} - c(t) - \delta.k(t) \ , \ k(0)=k_0 \text{ given.} \tag{5.13}$$

In Equation (5.13), A is a technology index, $\alpha \in (0,1)$ is the output – capital elasticity and δ is the depreciation rate of capital. Variable $k(t)$ represents the amount of physical capital available at each time moment t and $c(t)$ corresponds to real consumption (also at each moment t). The level of income arises in the equation as corresponding to the outcome of a neoclassical production function exhibiting decreasing marginal returns to capital. The variable $\dot{k}(t) \equiv dk(t)/dt$ defines the time increase on variable $k(t)$, in a similar way relatively to the notation in previous chapters. The capital accumulation rule (5.13) is similar to the one originally proposed by Solow (1956) and Swan (1956) to explain the process of economic growth.

To arrive to the objective function of the problem (to the utility function) notice that there is an income variable, but only a share of this income is consumed, in an amount $c(t)$. Variable $c(t)$ represents the total level of consumption at each time moment, with this consumption level respecting to both the consumption of non digital and of digital goods. The consumed quantity of the non digital good will be given by $x(t) = c(t) - \int_0^n p_i.z_i(t).di$, with p_i the price of each digital good (these prices are exogenous to the analysis) and $z_i(t) \in \{0,1\}$.

In order to proceed with the dynamic analysis of the model we need to present a specific functional form for the utility function; we assume that the demand for digital goods and for the non digital composite good is additively separable. For the non digital good one considers a CIES (constant intertemporal elasticity of substitution) function, which is common to find in this type of optimization problem:

$$U[x(t)] = \frac{1 - \left[c(t) - \int_0^n p_i.z_i(t).di \right]^{-(\theta-1)}}{\theta - 1}, \ \theta > 1 \tag{5.14}$$

For the digital goods, the previously considered functional form is maintained, but taking an innovation that allows the analysis to be closer to reality: one assumes that each digital good produces a different level of utility.

$$U[z_1(t),...,z_n(t)] = \left[\int_0^n u(z_i)^\rho .di \right]^{1/\rho}, \ u(z_i) = \begin{cases} 0, & z_i < 1 \\ u_i, & z_i \geq 1 \end{cases} \tag{5.15}$$

Thus, we will work with the utility function (5.16),

$$U[c(t)] = U[x(t)] + U[z_1(t),...,z_n(t)] \tag{5.16}$$

The optimal control problem under consideration will correspond to the intertemporal maximization of the flow of functions U,

$$Max \int_{0}^{+\infty} U[c(t)].e^{-\sigma.t}.dt \tag{5.17}$$

where parameter $\sigma > 0$ is a discount rate aimed at revealing that the present utility is more valued than the future utility. This maximization problem is subject to the resource constraint (5.13).

The defined optimal control problem is generally designated by Ramsey (1928) model, which allows essentially to establish a relation between present consumption and future consumption (today's capital accumulation allows for future consumption) that reveals the tension that exists between the final goal, attained through consumption, and the instrument that is necessary to attain it, which is savings and the corresponding investment that such savings allow for. The only novelty introduced into this structure is the consideration of digital goods in the composition of the consumption basket of the representative household.

To the optimal control problem corresponds the following current value Hamiltonian function:

$$\aleph(t) = U[c(t)] + q(t).[A.k(t)^{\alpha} - c(t) - \delta.k(t)] \tag{5.18}$$

with $q(t)$ a co-state variable, which can be interpreted as the shadow-price of physical capital. The following optimality conditions are found:

$$\lim_{t \to +\infty} q(t).e^{-\sigma.t}.k(t) = 0 \quad \text{(transversality condition)} \tag{5.19}$$

$$\aleph_c = 0 \Rightarrow \left[c(t) - \int_{0}^{1} p(z_i).di \right]^{-\theta} = q(t) \tag{5.20}$$

$$\dot{q}(t) = \sigma.q(t) - \aleph_k \Rightarrow \dot{q}(t) = \left[(\sigma + \delta) - \alpha.A.k(t)^{-(1-\alpha)} \right] q(t) \tag{5.21}$$

Differentiating the optimality condition (5.20) with respect to time, one obtains an expression for the time evolution of the consumption variable:

$$\dot{c}(t) = \frac{1}{\theta}.\left[\alpha.A.k(t)^{-(1-\alpha)} - (\sigma + \delta) \right]\left[c(t) - \int_{0}^{1} p(z_i).di \right] \tag{5.22}$$

Since the relation between the value of the non digital good and the digital goods is exogenous to the analysis, the endogenous relation of the model does not differ from the one of the original Ramsey model, i.e., the analysis concentrates on how consumption and capital time trajectories influence each other. To understand the relation between variables $k(t)$ and $c(t)$ one just has to resort to the already mentioned literature on this subject. Our analysis will focus on revealing that in the specified dynamic setting, utility maximization will require that the available income for consumption will be distributed between acquisition of the private good and purchase of digital goods.

Let us begin by inquiring about the long-run steady-state scenario. The computation of equilibrium values, from (5.13) and (5.22) allows finding the following pair of steady-state values:

$$\left(\bar{k},\bar{c}\right)=\left[\left(\frac{\alpha.A}{\sigma+\delta}\right)^{1/(1-\alpha)};\left(\frac{1}{\alpha}.\sigma+\frac{1-\alpha}{\alpha}.\delta\right)\bar{k}\right] \tag{5.23}$$

With the above equilibrium results, the homogeneous good will be consumed in the steady-state in the following quantity,

$$\bar{x}=\left(\frac{1}{\alpha}.\sigma+\frac{1-\alpha}{\alpha}.\delta\right)\bar{k}-\int_{0}^{n}p_{i}.\bar{z}_{i}.di \tag{5.24}$$

with $\bar{z}_{i}$, $i=1, ..., n$, the equilibrium value of each digital good, which, as we know, must assume value zero or value one.

It will be the utility maximization that will determine the equilibrium value of $x(t)$, since the maximization of utility will give the information about consuming each one of the digital goods given the trade-off that is established between the corresponding price and the utility they offer. An example helps in understanding this process. Imagine a scenario with two digital goods, such that in the long-run the level of utility is given by expression (5.25):

$$U(\bar{c})=\frac{1-(\bar{c}-p_{1}.z_{1}-p_{2}.z_{2})^{-(\theta-1)}}{\theta-1}+\left[(u_{1}.z_{1})^{\rho}+(u_{2}.z_{2})^{\rho}\right]^{1/\rho} \tag{5.25}$$

Four long-term situations are possible; the optimality problem should allow choosing the alternative generating a higher level of utility. The following results are possible:

$$U(\bar{c})_{[z_{1}=0,z_{2}=0]}=\frac{1-\bar{c}^{-(\theta-1)}}{\theta-1}$$

$$U(\bar{c})_{[z_{1}=1,z_{2}=0]}=\frac{1-(\bar{c}-p_{1})^{-(\theta-1)}}{\theta-1}+u_{1}$$

$$U(\bar{c})_{[z_{1}=0,z_{2}=1]}=\frac{1-(\bar{c}-p_{2})^{-(\theta-1)}}{\theta-1}+u_{2}$$

$$U(\bar{c})_{[z_{1}=1,z_{2}=1]}=\frac{1-(\bar{c}-p_{1}-p_{2})^{-(\theta-1)}}{\theta-1}+\left[u_{1}^{\rho}+u_{2}^{\rho}\right]^{1/\rho}$$

Considering, for instance, the following array of parameters:

$[\alpha \; A \; \sigma \; \delta \; p_1 \; p_2 \; \theta \; \rho \; u_1 \; u_2 \;]=$
$[0.25 \; 1 \; 0.025 \; 0.01 \; 0.8 \; 0.9 \; 2 \; 0.5 \; 0.3 \; 0.7]$

one can identify which is the long-run situation that allows for maximizing utility. Taking in consideration this set of values, one obtains the following steady-state values for the endogenous variables of the dynamic model: $\overline{k} = 13.756$ and $\overline{c} = 1.788$; the utility values are

$$U(\overline{c})_{[z_1=0, z_2=0]} = \frac{1-1.788^{-1}}{1} = 0.441$$

$$U(\overline{c})_{[z_1=1, z_2=0]} = \frac{1-(1.788-0.8)^{-1}}{1} + 0.3 = 0.288$$

$$U(\overline{c})_{[z_1=0, z_2=1]} = \frac{1-(1.788-0.9)^{-1}}{1} + 0.7 = 0.574$$

$$U(\overline{c})_{[z_1=1, z_2=1]} = \frac{1-(1.788-0.8-0.9)^{-1}}{1} + \left[\sqrt{0.3} + \sqrt{0.7}\right]^2 = -8.447$$

From the evaluation of the previous results one concludes that the best long-run option consists in acquiring the digital good z_2 but not z_1 (z_2 has a higher price than z_1 but the level of utility it offers to the consumer is also higher). In this case, the consumed quantity of the non digital good will be $\overline{x} = \overline{c} - p_2 = 0.888$. Thus, the basket $(\overline{x}, z_1, z_2) = (0.888; 0; 1)$ is preferable to any of the other three options, from the point of view of the consumer's utility, according to the specified utility function. The other three options are: $(\overline{x}, z_1, z_2) = (1.788; 0; 0)$, $(\overline{x}, z_1, z_2) = (0.988; 1; 0)$ and $(\overline{x}, z_1, z_2) = (0.088; 1; 1)$.

Besides the evaluation of utility in the steady-state, one can also pursue an analysis of transitional dynamics. The motion of variable $c(t)$ is given by Equation (5.22); besides this, one can also analyze which basket of goods should the individual choose at each time moment $t \in [0, +\infty)$ given the goal of intertemporal optimization; in other words, we are interested in knowing how consumption is distributed through time between non digital and digital goods.

Before undertaking this analysis, note a relevant point: one of the fundamental assumptions one has taken to define digital goods concerns the property of non rivalry in consumption, what means that for consuming n times a given digital good, the consumer needs to acquire the good only once, because its use does not damage the good concerning the possibility of future utilizations. Therefore, from the point of view of acquisition of the digital good this has to be made only once, and thus the price to pay by the digital good is restricted to some single moment t. In the analytical structure we are assuming, one is considering that at each time moment from the period in which the digital good is bought, it is necessary to pay a price p. This occurs in order to make the model tractable with the mathematical tools we are working with.

Two explanations for the reasonability of this assumption can be put forward: first, one can assume that the good is paid in fixed periodic payments, from the moment in which the good is acquired until the moment its possession ends; or, on the other hand, we can consider the digital good as a class of goods that are bought at every time moment, because at each period in time it will take new and different characteristics. For example, when we pay for a cable television channel, we are paying for a digital good that offers different contents over time, and therefore the acquisition of this digital good implies a continuous flow of payment in order to be possible to access it. This happens not only with television but with other digital contents, as the ones associated with the internet. Therefore, the various goods z_i that are analyzed in this section will be closer to what we acquire when subscribing a Cable TV channel or when accessing internet than when we buy in a specific time moment (and we pay in a specific time moment) a music CD or a computer game to use in a more or less long horizon.

Let us return to the example considering a specific set of parameter values and assume that the initial level of consumption is inferior to the equilibrium value: $c(0) < \overline{c}$. In this case, with the available numerical data, one observes in the beginning of the convergence process towards the equilibrium that the following consumption options exist:

- if $c(0) < 0.8$, the representative agent will not have resources to purchase, at the starting moment, any of the digital goods, and therefore the utility maximization requires the consumption of $x(t)=c(t)$ units of the homogeneous non digital good;
- if $0.8 < c(0) < 0.9$ or at the moment in which a value in this interval is attained, it is possible to consume good z_1 together with $x(t)$; the evaluation of utility in this circumstance, with the given values, reveals that a higher level of utility is attained when only $x(t)$ is consumed, relatively to the option of consumption of the digital good. Again, the optimal result implies that the consumed quantity of good x corresponds to the whole of the consumption value;
- in the interval $0.9 < c(0) < 1.7$ it is possible to consume zero or one digital goods but not the two, i.e., there are three consumption possibilities. From these possibilities, in the given interval, one withdraws the following strategy of utility maximization: to consume only the non digital good until $c(t) \approx 1.67$ and above this value to acquire digital good z_2 with the remaining consumption income directed to purchasing the non digital good: $x(t)=c(t)-0.9$;[5]
- for values of $c(t)$ in the interval $1.7 < c(t) < \overline{c}$, i.e., when the four possibilities of acquisition of digital goods exist, the result that maximizes utility will be the one we have found in the long-run situation: the digital good z_2 should be purchased and the remaining expenditure will be made in the non digital good.

---

[5] The point in which $c(t) \approx 1.67$ is the point where the level of utility when acquiring the digital good z_2 is equal to the level of utility of acquiring no digital goods and therefore consumption is concentrated solely on the acquisition of the non digital good. Below this point the utility of consuming just the non digital good is higher than the utility of consuming the digital good and the oppositve above such reference value. Equating both utility levels one will have $1-c(t)^{-1}=1.7-[c(t)-0.9]^{-1}$, what is equivalent to the second degree equation: $c(t)^2-0.9.c(t)-1.2857=0$; by solving this equation one finds two roots, with only the one with a positive sign having economic meaning; this corresponds effectively to $c(t) \approx 1.67$.

The above reasoning is just an illustrative example of how the growth of the income available to consumption in an economy that accumulates physical capital modifies the consumption options when goods with peculiar characteristics are taken into account. The main change is that at a given moment of the convergence process towards the equilibrium, there is a discontinuity because the agent will no longer use all her available income to consume non digital goods since one digital good begins to be purchased. The graphical representation of figures 5.3 and 5.4 contributes to understand this discontinuity or perturbation.

Figure 5.3 represents the consumption trajectories. Assuming that the aggregate level of consumption starts at a level $c(0)$ lower than the steady-state consumption level, it will converge through time to such value. Initially, the level of consumption has correspondence in the consumption of good $x(t)$ and therefore the trajectories of $c(t)$ and $x(t)$ are coincidental, until the point in which the income available for consumption attains value $c=1.67$. In the moment this fact occurs, part of the income is immediately channelled for acquisition of digital good z_2, with its price being $p_2=0.9$. The expenditure in good z_2, which until this moment was zero, will hereafter correspond to such price; simultaneously, the consumption of the non digital good will have to fall, corresponding from this point forward to the difference between the income available to consumption and the price that one pays at every moment to continue to acquire the digital good. Thus, through time, and after the fall in 0.9 units in the consumption of x that throws this value to 0.77, it will grow positively following the growth of income to consumption, until the equilibrium value, $\bar{x} = 0.888$, is attained. In the process of transition towards the steady-state, in what concerns variable z_2, this will always be consumed in one unit that maintains the same price 0.9, according to the assumptions of the model. Relatively to variable z_1, this digital good will never be purchased and therefore it will correspond forever to a zero share in the consumption expenditure.

Figure 5.4 highlights the relevance of the point of change in the composition of the consumption basket through the representation of the level of utility. Since the level of consumption grows in time, then utility will also grow. The property of decreasing marginal utility implicitly assumed in the functional form considered in (5.14) offers a justification for the concave shape of this function.

Until point $c(t) \approx 1.67$ it is followed the utility function providing, in this segment, the higher level of utility. After such point, the utility function in which goods x and z_2 are consumed will reveal large utility levels and therefore with a change in the consumed basket of goods another utility function representing higher satisfaction levels than the ones offered by the first utility function will be followed. This is evident when looking at the graphical representation.

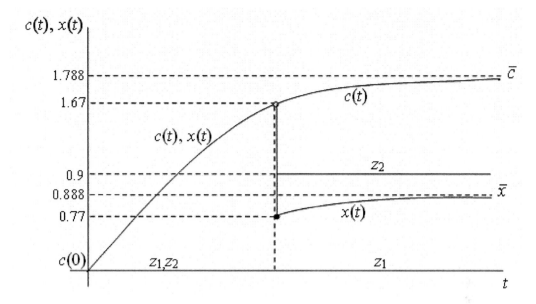

Figure 5.3. Consumption time trajectory in an optimal control model with digital and non digital goods.

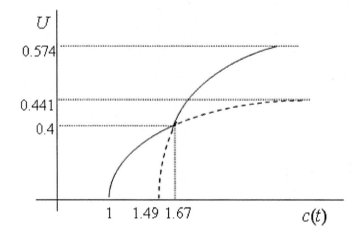

Figure 5.4. Utility function in an optimal control problem with digital and non digital goods.

5.4. PRODUCTION OF DIGITAL GOODS

Until this moment, we have considered the digital goods solely in the perspective of consumption utility. In the optimal control problem of the previous section, the economy produced indistinctively capital goods and consumption goods and among these we have found digital and non digital types of goods. In this setting, the choice among these types of goods at the productive level was completely driven by the consumption preferences, implying that the change of the production structure could be made immediately and without any costs. The choice of the goods to consume did not interfere with the production process and the accumulation of capital (firms were able to produce any type of goods in the exactly same circumstances).

In reality, the production process of the digital goods has peculiar features relatively to the production of non digital goods. These features relate to the definition of digital good that one has discussed earlier in this chapter. A theoretical structure concerning the production of digital goods should attend to the following points:

1) The digital goods are non rival, in opposition to non digital goods. Therefore, to the production of digital goods it is not necessary to subtract a share for consumption. The digital goods that can be re-used in production can serve also consumption purposes.

2) The digital goods are recombinant, what means that the production of a digital good will be as successful as the larger is the quantity of digital goods that already exists.

3) The digital goods are infinitely expansible, and thus only the production of the first unit matters. The production function of digital goods will be such that after the moment the first unit is produced, an infinite quantity of units of the good becomes available. In graphical terms, we will have an accumulation process of the digital good z as the one in figure 5.5.

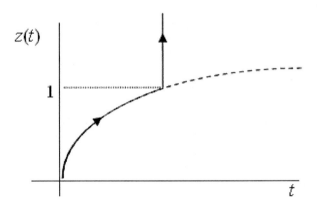

Figure 5.5. Production function of a digital good.

To the previous concept is also associated the idea that part of a digital good is equivalent to nothing from the point of view of its use to produce additional digital goods or to consume. The digital goods are discrete, meaning that not only at the level of consumption but also at the level of the reinvestment in production, only entire units of the good will be relevant.

In what follows, one builds an optimal control problem with two sectors: the first sector produces a non digital homogeneous good and the second sector generates digital goods. Relatively to this environment, we will not explore in detail the dynamics of the model; instead, we just sketch a possible analytical structure that can be used to further understand the impact of the digital goods' properties over the production system of the economy.

In the economy to assume, the sector that produces private goods will produce indistinctively (but not simultaneously) capital and consumption goods. The other sector will produce a digital good z_j, being implicitly considered that there already exists available in the economic system a set of digital goods until unit $j-1$. Being $c(t)$ the consumed quantity of the non digital good, u_i, $i=1, ..., j-1$, the utility generated individually by each one of the digital goods already produced and $u(z_j) = \begin{cases} 0, & z_j < 1 \\ u_j, & z_j \geq 1 \end{cases}$ the utility corresponding to good z_j, we can write the following utility function:

$$U[c(t), z_j] = \frac{1 - c(t)^{-(\theta-1)}}{\theta-1} + \left[\sum_{i=1}^{j-1} u_i^{\rho} + u(z_j)^{\rho}\right]^{1/\rho} \tag{5.26}$$

Two resource constraints complete the maximization problem $\int_0^{+\infty} U[c(t), z_j] e^{-\sigma.t} .dt$. These constraints will assume the following shapes:

$$\dot{k}(t) = A.[v(t).k(t)]^{\alpha} - c(t) - \delta.k(t) , k(0)=k_0 \text{ given.} \tag{5.27}$$

$$\dot{z}_j(t) = \left(\sum_{i=1}^{j-1} B_i\right)^{1/\gamma} .\{[1 - v(t)]k(t)\}^{\beta} , z_j(0)=0, z_j(t)<1, B_i>0, \gamma,\beta\in(0,1), 0<v(t)<1 \tag{5.28}$$

Relatively to these constraints, we highlight the following points:

- the capital is distributed among sectors, given variable $v(t)$. To produce private goods and to produce digital goods, capital is needed;
- parameter β is defined in a way that the contribution of capital to the production of digital goods reflects the existence of decreasing returns;
- the property of recombination will be present in the fact that it exists a positive contribution of the technology provided by already existing digital goods (these technological contributions are defined by B_i) to produce the considered digital good;
- the parameter γ guarantees that the effect of recombination is as much larger as the larger is the number of already available digital goods;
- The digital good is, as referred, a non rival good, implying that there is no need of subtracting any quantity to the production equation in order to consume;
- infinite expansibility implies that it only makes sense to produce z_j until the point in which one unit of this good exists; after this point the accumulation process is stopped $[z_j(t)=1 \Rightarrow \dot{z}_j(t) \to +\infty]$.

Considering some time interval, between t_0 and t_1, where only one digital good is produced, we would have two optimal control problems: one while the production of the digital good is not yet complete and another one with such good fully integrated in the utility function.

Thus, in a first phase (from t_0 to $t'_0 <t_1$) one would be interested in solving

$$Max \int_0^{t'_0} \left[\frac{1 - c(t)^{-(\theta-1)}}{\theta - 1} + \left(\sum_{i=1}^{j-1} u_i^{\rho} \right)^{1/\rho} \right] . e^{-\sigma.(t'_0 - t_0)} . dt$$

subject to : $\dot{k}(t) = A.[v(t).k(t)]^{\alpha} - c(t) - \delta.k(t), \ k(t_0) = k_0$ given

$$\dot{z}_j(t) = \left(\sum_{i=1}^{j-1} B_i \right)^{1/\gamma} . \{[1 - v(t)]k(t)\}^{\beta}, \ z_j(t_0) = 0$$

with t'_0 the moment in which the production of the digital good is completed. In this problem there are two state variables [$k(t)$ and $z_j(t)$] and two control variables [$c(t)$ and $v(t)$]. These last two are the ones that the representative consumer has the possibility of manipulating in order to promote her utility maximization objective. The other two are state variables in the sense that the rule for their change is given from the start by the two differential equations.

In a second phase, with the digital good already produced, we have a Ramsey model with the state and the control variable being, respectively, $k(t)$ and $c(t)$. Now, $z_j(t)=1$ and $v(t)=1$.

$$Max \int_{t'_0}^{t_1} \left[\frac{1 - c(t)^{-(\theta-1)}}{\theta - 1} + \left(\sum_{i=1}^{j} u_i^{\rho} \right)^{1/\rho} \right] . e^{-\sigma.(t_1 - t'_0)} . dt$$

subject to : $\dot{k}(t) = A.k(t)^{\alpha} - c(t) - \delta.k(t), \ k(t'_0) = k_0$ given

Both problems can be solved through the use of the Pontryagin principle, however we do not develop such study here. The essential point has been made: the main properties of the digital goods can be integrated in an intertemporal model of consumption and capital accumulation. The main obstacle relating the practical use of the theoretical structure of this section is that the digital goods are not produced in different moments of time, but often simultaneously. To overcome this difficulty, the problem can be understood sequentially, i.e., the second form of the problem will not tend to persist in time since a new good $j+1$ will begin to be produced, requiring that a part of the physical capital available in the economy must be allocated to the new digital good's production process; the production of this new good will benefit from an improved efficiency, given that it can make use of the technology B_j which allowed to produce the preceding digital good, z_j.

This chapter has highlighted the unique characteristics of digital goods and the way in which these change the main characteristics of the economic processes of production, transaction and consumption. Non rivalry, infinite expansibility, discretion, a-spatiality and recombination are the properties that distinguish these goods from the ones traditionally used to explain economic phenomena. To understand the impact of the peculiar properties of the digital goods or knowledge goods is a fundamental point in a moment of our history in which such goods have a large and increasing weight in the economic system, namely in the developed world.

The first main consequence of the different nature of the digital goods regarding the analysis of the economic system relates, as one has discussed, the non convexity of preferences for digital goods. The non convexity property implies that the utility theory developed by the economic science throughout the last few decades needs to be adapted to a new class of goods defined as bitstrings not only as the result of their physical shape but also because of the way in which they become available to be consumed: the utility of consumption of digital goods can be reduced to the utility of consuming, or not, an entire and complete unit of the good.

Despite one having stressed the fundamental differences between digital goods and the private goods for which different quantities represent, in general, different levels of utility, one should also recognize that the increasing existence and relevance of knowledge goods in the economic system does not change the basic philosophy underlying the fundamental problems addressed by economics. As one as perceived, the consumption utility problem, the one we have emphasized most, is the same independently of the considered type of goods; as always, the representative agent will choose an optimal allocation for the available resources in order to maximize utility.

Therefore, the nature of the goods changes but the nature of the problem remains the same. If one assumes that digital goods can be traded in the market, i.e., assuming that there exists some excludability mechanism imposing property rights on the knowledge goods, the consumer choices will be limited to the consumer goods acquisition capacity and the purchasing of digital goods will just imply a contraction of the resource constraint, such that less non digital goods will be consumed. The producer problem, of profit maximization, was not directly addressed in this chapter but it would mean in the same way the need to equate revenues and costs independently of the type of goods in consideration.

The introduction of a dynamic component, in sections 5.3 and 5.4, does not change the basic problem: choices depend on the utility attributed to the consumption of each good, independently of being digital or not, and on the productive capacity, which in the dynamic case evolves in time according to the investment and production capabilities. The main innovation coming from the intertemporal scenario is that this allows at any initial time moment, $t=0$, to establish which is the basket of goods to be consumed in the future and to know if this basket is maintained through time or if there is a substitution of the consumption of non digital goods by digital ones (or vice-versa); the setup also allows to know which digital goods should be consumed at each time moment, given their price and the measure of the utility they generate.

The chapter ended up by giving special attention to the demand side; however, some of the properties of the digital goods are strongly associated with specificities relating their production process. Particularly, the infinite expansibility and recombination properties turn evident substantial differences relatively to the production process of private goods. Section 5.4 has pointed some modelling peculiarities associated with the production of digital goods, and by doing it, it has revealed the need to separate the phase of production from the phase of consumption, because as long as it is being produced the digital good is always a 'zero' and its production requires it to be a 'one'.

The digital goods not only introduce a new dimension in the study of the economic system, but also establish a strong link between economics and communication. The digital goods are, in some sense, communication-goods, i.e., they are goods relatively to which transaction and consumption are inseparable from the communication process, only possible thanks to the new media or communication channels developed in recent years.

5.5. APPLICATIONS

Application 1

<u>A</u>ssume the maximization problem (5.9) and the following vector of parameters: $[\rho \ p_1 \ p_2 \ p_x \ y]=[0.25 \ 1 \ 2 \ 2 \ 3]$.

a) Transform (5.9) into a maximization problem without a constraint;
b) Evaluate the several possible outcomes, in terms of digital goods acquisition, and identify the optimal result.

A. Transform (5.9) into a Maximization Problem without a Constraint
For the considered parameters, the assumed problem is reduced to:

$$Max \, U(z_1, z_2, x) = \left(z_1 + z_2 + x^{0.25}\right)^4 \text{ subject to } 3 \geq z_1 + 2.z_2 + 2.x \, .$$

Variable x corresponds to the quantity of some non digital good; z_1 and z_2 will be digital goods and therefore they can only assume the values zero or one. According with the data of the exercise, the price of the non digital good will be identical to the price of the digital good 2, and twice the price of the digital good 1.

Assuming that all the available income (y) is directed to the acquisition of goods in order to maximize utility, the optimization problem can be rewritten by replacing in the corresponding expression variable x by its equivalent in terms of digital goods. The solicited problem will then be the following:

$$Max \, U(z_1, z_2, x) = \left[z_1 + z_2 + (1.5 - 0.5.z_1 - z_2)^{0.25}\right]^4 .$$

B. Evaluate the Outcomes and Identify the Optimal Result
The digital goods are characterized by the fact that they are consumed only in entire units. Given the non rivalry property it will not matter the acquisition of more than one unit; this means that only two scenarios become relevant: the consumption or the absence of consumption of each digital good. Four cases are possible:

(i) the agent does not acquire any digital good: $U(0,0)=1$ and $x=1.5$;
(ii) the agent acquires digital good z_1: $U(1,0)=16$ and $x=1$;
(iii) the agent acquires digital good z_2: $U(0,1)=11.487$ and $x=0.5$;
(iv) the agent acquires the two digital goods: $U(1,1)=16$ and $x=0$.

The optimal result will be the one that corresponds to a higher utility level. Observing the various alternatives, one concludes that two results are equally optimal: the acquisition of both digital goods (what implies having no access to any quantity of the non digital good) or the acquisition of only good z_1 and not z_2 (what allows having access to the non digital good in a quantity $x=1$).

Application 2

Consider the dynamic optimization problem of section 5.3. In this section, an example is presented by defining a vector of parameters, where $A=1$ corresponds to a technology index. Assume a technological shock that doubles the production efficiency: $A'=2$. Study the impact of this perturbation over the model's dynamics.

In section 5.3 one has considered an intertemporal consumption utility maximization model, subject to a productive resources constraint. The output can be directed to the accumulation of productive inputs, which will be used again in production, and for consumption. The consumption options are of two types: digital and non digital goods. The steady-state values relating to the accumulated capital and to consumption are given by expressions (5.23) and (5.24), with this last one specifying the amount of the non digital good that is consumed, having in consideration the acquired digital goods.

In the specific presented example, two digital goods $z_1(t)$ and $z_2(t)$ and a non digital good $x(t)$ are assumed. The new steady-state values, for $A'=2$, will be $\bar{k}' = 34.663$ and $\bar{c}' = 4.506$. A twice as large technological capacity implies significant increases in the steady-state values; one observes that $\bar{k}'/\bar{k} = 2.52$ and $\bar{c}'/\bar{c} = 2.52$, i.e., the new equilibrium values correspond to 2.52 times the pre-perturbation values.

The equilibrium utility values can also be computed; one obtains:

$$U(\bar{c})_{[z_1=0,z_2=0]} = \frac{1-4.506^{-1}}{1} = 0.778$$

$$U(\bar{c})_{[z_1=1,z_2=0]} = \frac{1-(4.506-0.8)^{-1}}{1} + 0.3 = 1.030$$

$$U(\bar{c})_{[z_1=0,z_2=1]} = \frac{1-(4.506-0.9)^{-1}}{1} + 0.7 = 1.423$$

$$U(\bar{c})_{[z_1=1,z_2=1]} = \frac{1-(4.506-0.8-0.9)^{-1}}{1} + \left[\sqrt{0.3}+\sqrt{0.7}\right]^2 = 2.755$$

Comparing the results now obtained with the example of the chapter, one observes that the change in the productive efficiency has a relevant impact over choices. While for $A=1$ one has verified that the best option respected the acquisition of digital good z_2 and not the acquisition of z_1, now the best long-term option consists in consuming both digital goods; this is the way to proceed if one wants to maximize utility.

In this circumstance, the equilibrium quantity of the non digital good that is consumed is $\bar{x}=\bar{c} - p_1 - p_2 = 4.506 - 0.8 - 0.9 = 2.806$. The basket $(\bar{x},z_1,z_2) = (2.806; 1; 1)$ will be the preferred one in the long-run; it will be preferred relatively to the other three baskets: $(\bar{x},z_1,z_2) = (4.506; 0; 0)$; $(\bar{x},z_1,z_2) = (3.706; 1; 0)$; and $(\bar{x},z_1,z_2) = (3.606; 0; 1)$.

Similarly to what was done in the study undertaken in section 5.3, one can explore the process of dynamic transition. In the present case, we will be comparing, for different values of $c(t)$ [between $c(0)=0$ and $\bar{c} = 4.506$], the best alternative in terms of utility, knowing that,

$$U[c(t)]_{[z_1=0,z_2=0]} = c(t)-1;$$

$$U[c(t)]_{[z_1=1,z_2=0]} = 1.3.c(t)-2.04;$$

$$U[c(t)]_{[z_1=0,z_2=1]} = 1.7.c(t)-2.53;$$

$$U[c(t)]_{[z_1=1,z_2=1]} = 2.917.c(t)-5.959$$

Comparing these values, one observes that until $c(t)=2.143$ the best option, concerning utility maximization, consists in buying exclusively the non digital good; in the interval $2.143<c(t)<2.817$, the consumer will purchase digital good z_2, but not z_1, with the remaining income used to purchase the non digital good; for $c(t)>2.817$, it is optimal to buy the two digital goods and this result will be maintained throughout time until the steady-state is reached.

The characterized trajectories are presented graphically.

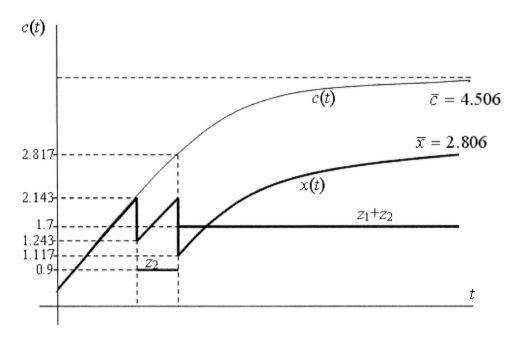

This figure should be compared with 5.3. The increase in the productive efficiency has significantly disturbed the time evolution of the variables. In particular, the non digital good variable suffers two falls, as the result of the time moments in which a part of the resources begin to be channelled towards the acquisition of digital goods.

Application 3

In what sense one can define a digital good as a communication-good?

Throughout this chapter we have discussed the notion of digital good. The set of characteristics that defines it has driven us to the concept of bitstring, that is, to the idea of sequences of zeros and ones that can be transmitted at any distance, without imposing any physical transfer. Under this interpretation, a digital good can be conceived simply as the contents of a transmitted message.

In chapter 1 one has argued that the message is the central element of the communication process. To communicate is essentially to send and to receive messages with some kind of contents. Therefore, the economics of the digital goods is in fact closer to the notion of communication than the economics related to the physical transaction of goods and services; this last one requires communication in order for transactions to take place, however it is possible to distinguish without ambiguities the market transaction from the interaction process that allows it.

To trade digital goods involves an intrinsic communication process. To communicate means sending and receiving messages, with the contents of these messages possibly being a good with economic value, i.e., possibly being digital goods. Thus, the digital goods are communication-goods in the sense that they eventually constitute the contents of some human interaction process.

LIST OF VARIABLES AND PARAMETERS

$a_i(t)$:   expected benefit of option i (chapter 2);

$a_i(Y)$:   additional reward of agent X, when agent Y chooses option i (chapter 2);

$a(t)$:   expected benefit (chapter 3);

a: production function parameter (chapter 4 – application 1);

b: intensity of the decreasing returns in the learning function (chapter 2);

$b_i(X)$:   additional reward of agent Y, when agent X chooses option i (chapter 2);

$c(t)$:   consumption level (chapter 5);

g: parameter of the communicational efficiency model (chapter 5);

$h(t)$:   quantity of human capital per unit of physical capital (chapter 4);

$i_h(t)$:   investment in human capital per unit of human capital (chapter 4);

$i_k(t)$:   investment in physical capital per unit of physical capital (chapter 4);

$i_h(t)$:   investment in organizational capital per unit of organizational capital (chapter 4);

j: combination of parameters, in the learning model (chapter 2);

j_{12}, j_{21}:   combinations of parameters, in the social interaction model (chapter 2);

$k(t)$:   cognitive resources (chapter 3);

$k(t)$:   physical capital (chapter 5);

m: number of digital goods (chapter 5);

n: number of private goods (chapter 5);

$o(t)$:   quantity of organizational capital per unit of physical capital (chapter 4);

$p(t)$:   shadow-price of the cognitive resources variable (chapter 3);

p_{11}, p_{21}:   elements of the eigenvector associated to the negative eigenvalue (chapter 3, 4);

$p_h(t)$:   shadow-price of variable $h(t)$ (chapter 4);

$p_o(t)$:   shadow-price of variable $o(t)$ (chapter 4);

$p_K(t), p_H(t), p_O(t)$:   shadow-prices in the model with endogenous physical capital (chapter 4);

p_x: price of good x (chapter 5);

p_z: price of good z (chapter 5);

$q(t)$:   shadow-price of physical capital (chapter 5);

t: time variable (all chapters);

u_i: utility produced by good i (chapter 5);

v: share of capital allocated to the production of additional capital (chapter 5);

$w(t)$:   wage rate (chapter 4);
$x_i(t)$:   probability of choice associated to action i (chapter 2);
$\mathbf{x}(t)$:   distribution of choices (chapter 2);
x_i: quantity of the private good i (chapter 5);
$\mathbf{x}^i$:   vector of private goods (chapter 5);
$y_i(t)$:   probability of choice of action i by agent Y (chapter 2);
$y(t)$:   cognitive resources added at each time moment (chapter 3);
$y(t)$:   evel of production per unit of physical capital (chapter 4);
y: budgetary endowment of a representative agent (chapter 5);
$z(t)$:   cognitive resources used to process information and evaluate choices (chapter 3);
z_i: digital good i (chapter 5);
$\mathbf{z}^i$:   vector of digital goods (chapter 5).

$A_i(X)$:   reward of agent X, when choosing option i (chapter 2);
A: parameter of communicational efficiency (chapter 3);
A: technological level of the firm (chapter 4);
A: technology index (chapter 5);
$B_i(Y)$:   reward of agent Y, when choosing option i (chapter 2);
B_i: production technology of the digital goods (chapter 5);
$\mathbf{D}$:   slopes' matrix (chapter 3);
E: steady-state point (chapter 3);
E':   post-perturbation steady-state point (chapter 3);
$H(t)$:   human capital (chapter 4);
$I_h(t)$:   investment in human capital (chapter 4);
$I_k(t)$:   investment in physical capital (chapter 4);
$I_o(t)$:   investment in organizational capital (chapter 4);
J: Jacobian matrix in the learning model (chapter 2);
$\mathbf{J}$:   Jacobian matrix in the social interaction model (chapter 2);
J: Jacobian matrix in the model of optimization of the communication result (chapter 3);
J: Jacobian matrix in the model of profit maximization (chapter 4);
$J(X)$:   exogenous perturbations matrix (chapter 3);
$J(\delta_o)$:   vector of perturbations over δ_o (chapter 4);
$J(\gamma)$:   vector of perturbations over γ (chapter 4);
$K(t)$:   communication function (chapter 3);
$K(t)$:   physical capital (chapter 4);
N: number of choice options (chapter 2);
N: number of agents in the model of communicational interdependency (chapter 3);
$O(t)$:   stock of organizational capital (chapter 4);
P_1, P_2:   eigenvectors (chapter 3, 4);
$Q_i(t)$:   memory variable (chapter 2);
$\mathbf{Q}(t)$:   vector of memory variables (chapter 2);
$\mathbf{R}$:   set of real numbers (chapter 5);

$U[c(t)]$:   consumption utility function (chapter 5);
$U(\mathbf{x})$:   utility function for non digital goods (chapter 5);
$U(\mathbf{x},\mathbf{z})$:   utility function for digital and non digital goods (chapter 5);
X: agent that undertakes choices (chapter 2);
Y: agent that undertakes choices (chapter 2);
$Y(t)$:   production level of the firm (chapter 4);
Z: set $\{0,1\}$ (chapter 5).

α: memory loss parameter (chapter 2);
α_X: memory loss parameter (agent X) (chapter 2);
α_Y: memory loss parameter (agent Y) (chapter 2);
α: output - capital elasticity (chapter 5);
β, $\beta(t)$:   intensity of choice (chapter 2);
β_X: intensity of choice (agent X) (chapter 2);
β_Y: intensity of choice (agent Y) (chapter 2);
β: output – capital elasticity for digital goods (chapter 5);
γ: physical capital growth rate (chapter 4);
γ: parameter of the production function of digital goods (chapter 5);
δ: rate of knowledge obsolescence (chapter 2);
δ_k: depreciation rate of cognitive resources (chapter 3);
δ_A: rate of efficiency loss in communication (chapter 3);
δ_k: depreciation rate of physical capital (chapter 4);
δ_h: depreciation rate of human capital (chapter 4);
δ_o: depreciation rate of organizational capital (chapter 4);
δ: depreciation rate of capital (chapter 5);
ε: parameter translating the impact of organizational capital over the accumulation of human capital (chapter 4);
ζ: concavity parameter of the communication function (chapter 3);
θ: utility function parameter (chapter 5);
κ: initial level of physical capital held by the firm (chapter 4);
λ_i: eigenvalue of the Jacobian matrix (chapters 2, 3, 4);
μ: output – human capital elasticity (chapter 4);
ξ: concavity parameter of the communicational efficiency function (chapter 3);
$\pi(t)$:   firm's profit per physical capital unit (chapter 4);
ρ: discount rate of the future expected benefit (chapter 3);
ρ: discount rate of future profits (chapter 4);
ρ: utility function parameter (chapter 5);
σ: discount rate of consumption utility (chapter 5);
τ: positive constant (chapter 4);
$\phi(t)$:   ratio between probabilities of choice (chapter 2);
ψ: parameter of the production function (chapter 4 –application 1);
$\varphi(t)$:   ratio between probabilities of choice for agent Y (chapter 2).

$\Pi(t)$:   firm's profit (chapter 4).

$\aleph(t)$:   Hamiltonian function (chapters 3, 4, 5).

REFERENCES

Aigrain, P. (1997). "Attention, Media, Value and Economics." *First Monday*, vol. 2, no. 9. http://www.firstmonday.dk/issues/ issue2_9/aigrain/index.html

Anderson, S.; A. Palma and J. Thisse (1993). *Discrete Choice Theory of Product Differentiation*. Cambridge, Mass.: MIT Press.

Arrow, K. J. (1974). *The Limits of Organization*. New York: Norton.

Arrow, K. J. (1985). "Informational Structure of the Firm." *American Economic Review*, vol. 75, pp. 303-307.

Arrow, K. J. and G. Debreu (1954). "Existence of Equilibrium for a Competitive Economy." *Econometrica*, vol.22, pp. 265-290.

Bárány, I. (1992). "Fair Distribution Protocols or How the Players Replace Fortune." *Mathematics of Operations Research*, vol. 53, pp. 327-340.

Ben-Porath, E. (2003). "Cheap Talk in Games with Incomplete Information." *Journal of Economic Theory*, vol. 108, pp. 45-71.

Barro, R. J. and X. Sala-i-Martin (1995). *Economic Growth*. New York: McGraw-Hill.

Becker, G. S. (1964). *Human Capital*. New York: Columbia University Press.

Benkard, C. L. (1999). *Learning and Forgetting: the Dynamics of Aircraft Production*. Stanford University Graduate School of Business.

Berger, C. R. (1992). "Curiouser and Curiouser Curios." *Communication Monographs*, vol. 59, pp. 101-107.

Berger, C. R. and T. Luckmann (1966). *The Social Construction of Reality: a Treatise in the sociology of Knowledge*. Garden City, NY: Doubleday.

Berlo, D. K. (1960). *Communication: an Introduction to Theory and Practice*. New York: Holt, Rinehart e Winston.

Bourdieu, P. (1986). "The Forms of Capital." in J. G. Richardson (ed.), *Handbook for Theory and Research for the Sociology of Education*, pp. 241-258.

Brock, W. A. and S. Durlauf (2001). "Discrete Choice with Social Interactions." *Review of Economic Studies*, vol. 68, pp. 235-260.

Brock, W. A. and S. Durlauf (2003). "A Multinomial Choice Model with Social Interactions." *The Economy as an Evolving Complex System III*, L. Blume and S. Durlauf, eds., Oxford University Press.

Brock, W. A. and C. H. Hommes (1997). "A Rational Route to Randomness." *Econometrica*, vol. 65, pp. 1059-1095.

Brock, W. A. and C. H. Hommes (1998). "Heterogeneous Beliefs and Routes to Chaos in a Simple Asset Pricing Model." *Journal of Economic Dynamics and Control*, vol. 22, pp.1235-1274.

Brock, W. A. and C. H. Hommes (2002). *Heterogeneous Beliefs and Routes to Complex Dynamics in Asset Pricing Models with Price Contingent Contracts*. Amsterdam: CeNDEF working paper.

Brown, J. R. and A. Goolsbee (2002). "Does the Internet Make Markets More Competitive? Evidence from the Life Insurance Industry." *Journal of Political Economy*, vol. 110, pp. 481-507.

Browne, C. B. (1998). "Linux and Decentralized Development." *First Monday*, vol. 3, n° 3. http://www.firstmonday.dk/issues /issue3_3/browne /index.html

Caballero, R. and A. Jaffe (1993). "How High are the Giants' Shoulders: an Empirical Assessment of Knowledge Spillovers and Creative Destruction in a Model of Economic Growth." In O. Blanchard and S. Fischer, eds., *National Bureau of Economic Research Macroeconomics Annual*, vol. 8. MIT Press.

Chen, J. (2004). *An Entropy Theory of Value*. University of Northern British Columbia.

Cherry, C. (1978). *On Human Communication* (3ª edição). Cambridge, MA: MIT Press.

Chowhdry, B. and M. J. Garmaise (2003). *Organization Capital and Intrafirm Communication*. Anderson Graduate School of Management, University of California.

Cover, T. M. and J. A. Thomas (1991). *Elements of Information Theory*. New York: Willey Series in Telecommunications.

Craig, R. T. (1993). "Why Are There So Many Communication Theories?" *Journal of Communication*, vol. 43, pp. 26-33.

Crémer, J. (1993). "Language and Shared Knowledge." *Industrial and Corporate Change*, vol. 2, pp. 351-386.

De Marzo, P.; D. Vayanos and J. Zwiebel (2003). "Persuasion Bias, Social Influence and Uni-Dimensional Opinions." *Quarterly Journal of Economics*, vol. 118, pp. 909-968.

Devito, J. A. (1986). *The Communication Handbook: a Dictionary*. New York: Harper & Row.

Durlauf, S. (2003). "Neighborhood Effects." In J. V. Henderson and J. F. Thisse (eds.), *Handbook of Regional and Urban Economics, vol. 4*. Amsterdam: North-Holland.

Durlauf, S. and E. Cohen-Cole (2004). *Social Interaction Models*. University of Winsconsin.

Feldman, D. P. and J. P. Crutchfield (2002). "Structural Information in Two-Dimensional Patterns: Entropy Convergence and Excess Entropy." *Santa Fe Institute Working Paper*.

Forges, F. (1986). "An Approach to Communication Equilibria." *Econometrica*, vol. 54, pp. 1375-1385.

Forges, F. (1990). "Universal Mechanisms." *Econometrica*, vol. 58, pp. 1341-1364.

Freund, C. and M. Weinhold (2002). "The Internet and International Trade in Services." *American Economic Review*, vol. 92, pp. 236-240.

Gabaix, X. and D. Laibson (2004). "Bounded Rationality and Directed Cognition." *MIT and Harvard University working paper*.

Garicano, L. (2000). "Hierarchies and the Organization of Knowledge in Production." *Journal of Political Economy*, vol. 108, pp. 874-904.

Ghosh, R. A. (1998). "Cooking Pot Markets: an Economic Model for the Trade in Free Goods and Services on the Internet." *First Monday*, vol. 3, n 3. http://www.firstmonday.dk/issues /issue3_3/ghosh /index.html

Glaeser, E.; B. Sacerdote and J. Scheinkman (1996). "Crime and Social Interactions." *Quarterly Journal of Economics*, vol. 111, pp. 507-548.

Goldhaber, M. H. (1997). "What's the Right Economics for Cyberspace?" *First Monday*, vol. 2, n 7. http:// www.firstmonday.dk/issues/issue2_7/goldhaber/index.html

Gomes, O. (2004). "Os Bens Digitais e a Dinâmica da Weightless Economy." *Global Economics and Management*, vol. IX, n 2/2004, pp. 53-64.

Gomes, O. (2007). "Investment in Organizational Capital." *Managerial and Decision Economics*, vol. 28, pp. 107-113.

Gomes, O. (2009). *Principles of Economic Dynamics*. Hyderabad, Andhra Pradesh: ICFAI university press.

Green, J. O. (1997). *Message Production: Advances in Communication Theory*. Mahwah, NJ: Erlbaum.

Gossner, O.; P. Hernández and A. Neyman (2006). "Optimal Use of Communication Resources." *Econometrica*, vol. 74, pp. 1603-1636.

Habermas, J. (1981). *The Theory of Communicative Action: Reason and the Rationalization of Society*. Boston: Beacon Press.

Habermas, J. (1987). "Excursus on Luhmann's Appropriation of the Philosophy of the Subject Through Systems Theory." In *The Philosophical Discourse of Modernity: Twelve Lectures*, pp. 368-385. Cambridge, MA: MIT Press.

Hale, J. K. and H. Koçak (1991). *Dynamics and Bifurcation*. New York: Springer-Verlag.

Heath, R. L. and J. Bryant (2000). *Human Communication Theory and Research: Concepts, Contexts and Challenges*. New Jersey: Lawrence Erlbaum Associates.

Hermalin, B. (2001). "Economics and Language." In S. Cartwright et al. (Eds.), *Handbook of Organizational Culture and Climate*. Chichester: John Wiley and Sons.

Hirokawa, R. Y. (1990). "The Role of Communication in Group Decision-Making Efficacy: a Task-Contingency Perspective." *Small Group Research*, vol. 21, pp. 190-204.

Jehle, G. A. and P. J. Reny (2001). *Advanced Microeconomic Theory*. Second edition. Boston: Addison Wesley Longman.

Kahneman, D. (2003). "Maps of Bounded Rationality: Psychology for Behavioral Economics." *American Economic Review*, vol. 93, pp. 1449-1475.

Katz, D. and R. L. Kahn (1966). *The Social Psychology of Organizations*. New York: Willey.

Kreps, D. M. (1990). "Corporate Culture and Economic Theory." Em J. Alt e K. Shepsle (Eds.), *Perspectives on Positive Political Economy*. Cambridge: Cambridge University Press.

Krippendorff, K. (1975). "Information Theory." Em G. J. Hanneman e W. J. McEwen (eds.), *Communication and Behavior*, pp. 351-389. Reading, MA: Addison-Wesley.

Krippendorff, K. (1977). "Information Systems Theory and Research: an Overview." In B. D. Ruben (ed.), *Communication Yearbook 1*, pp. 149-171. New Brunswick, NJ: Transaction Books.

Kroon, S. M. A.; E. Pierick; J. J. Vlieger; G. B. C. Backus and R. P. King (2002). *Social Capital and Communication*. Agricultural Economics Research Institute, the Hague.

Lachman, M.; M. E. J. Newman and C. Moore (1999). The Physical Limits of Communication or Why Any Sufficiently Advanced Technology is Indistinguishable from Noise. Santa Fe Institute working paper.

Leydesdorff, L. (2000). "Luhmann, Habermas and the Theory of Communication." Systems Research and Behavioral Science, vol. 17, pp. 273-288.

Lorenz, H. W. (1993). Nonlinear Dynamical Economics and Chaotic Motion. 2nd edition, Berlin: Springer-Verlag.

Lyne, J. (1998). "Philosophical Approaches to Communication Theory." Journal of Communication, vol. 48, pp. 153-157.

Manski, C. (1993). "Identification of Endogenous Social Effects: the Reflection Problem." Review of Economic Studies, vol. 60, pp. 531-542.

Manski, C. and D. McFadden (1981). Structural Analysis of Discrete Data with Econometric Applications. Cambridge, Mass.: MIT Press.

Maznevski, M. (1994). "Understanding our Differences: Performances in Decision-Making Groups with Diverse Members." Human Relations, vol. 47, pp. 531-552.

McFadden, D. (1973). "Conditional Logit Analysis of Qualitative Choice Behavior." In Frontiers in Econometrics, ed. P. Zarembka, pp.105-142. New York: Academic Press.

McLaughlin, M. L. (1984). Conversation: How Talk is Organized. Newbury Park, CA: Sage.

McLuhan, M. (1964). Understanding Media: the Extensions of Man. New York: New American Library.

McQuail, D. (1987). "Functions of Communication: a Nonfunctionalist Overview." In C. R. Berger and S. H. Chaffee (eds.), Handbook of Communication Science, pp. 327-349. Newbury Park, CA: Sage.

Mead, G. H. (1934). Mind, Self and Society. Chicago: University of Chicago Press.

Mortensen, C. D., with C. M. Ayres (1997). Miscommunication. Thousand Oaks, CA: Sage.

Murteira, M.; I. Nicolau; V. Mendes and A. Martins (2001). Informational Services and Transition for the Knowledge Economy in Portugal. Lisbon: GEPE and IAPMEI.

Myerson, R. B. (1986). "Multistage Games with Communication." Econometrica, vol. 54, pp. 323-358.

Nahapiet, J. and S. Ghoshal (1998). "Social Capital, Intellectual Capital and the Organizational Advantage." Academy of Management Review, vol. 2, pp. 242-266.

Nonaka, I. and H. Takeuchi (1995). The Knowledge-Creating Company. New York: Oxford University Press.

Pearce, W. B. and V. E. Cronen (1980). Communication, Action, and Meaning. New York, Praeger.

Pondy, L. R. and I. I. Mitroff (1979). "Beyond Open Systems Models of Organization." In L. L. Cummings and B. M. Staw (eds.), Research in Organizational Behavior, vol. 1, Greenwhich, CT: JAI Press.

Prescott, E. C. and M. Visscher (1980). "Organization Capital." Journal of Political Economy, vol. 88, pp. 446-461.

Quah, D. (1998). "A Weightless Economy." The UNESCO Courier, December.

Quah, D. (2001). "Technology Dissemination and Economic Growth: Some Lessons for the New Economy." CEPR discussion paper 3207.

Quah, D. (2002). "Digital Goods and the New Economy." Working paper. London: LSE Economics Department.

Radner, R. (1993). "The Organization of Decentralized Information Processing." Econometrica, vol. 61, pp. 1109-1146.

Ramsey, F. (1928). "A Mathematical Theory of Saving." Economic Journal, vol. 38, pp. 543-559.

Rogers, E. M. and D. L. Kincaid (1981). Communication Networks: Toward a New Paradigm for Research. New York: Free Press.

Romer, P. M. (2000). "Thinking and Feeling." *American Economic Review*, vol. 90, pp. 439-443.

Sato, Y.; E. Akiyama and J. P. Crutchfield (2004). "Stability and Diversity in Collective Adaptation." *Santa Fe Institute Working Paper*.

Sato, Y.; E. Akiyama and J. D. Farmer (2002). "Chaos in Learning a Simple Two-Person Game." *Proceedings of the National Academy of Science*, vol. 99, pp. 4748-4751.

Sato, Y. and J. P. Crutchfield (2003). "Coupled Replicator Equations for the Dynamics of Learning in Multiagent Systems." *Physical Review E*, vol. 67, 015206(R).

Schans, J. W. (2001). *Governance of Marine Resources. Conceptual Clarifications and Two Case Studies*. Delft: Eburon.

Schramm, W. (1954). "How Communication Works". In W. Schramm (ed.), *The Process and Effects of Mass Communication*, pp. 3-26. Urbana, IL: University of Illinois Press.

Schramm, W. (1973). *Men, Messages and Media*. New York: Harper & Row.

Schultz, T. W. (1961). "Investment in Human Capital." *American Economic Review*, vol. 51, pp. 1-17.

Shannon, C. (1948). "A Mathematical Theory of Communication." *The Bell System Technical Journal*, vol. 27, pp. 379-423, pp. 623-656.

Shannon, C. and W. Weaver (1949). *The Mathematical Theory of Communication*. Urbana, IL: University of Illinois Press.

Sheperd, G. J. (1999). "Advances in Communication Theory: a Critical Review." *Journal of Communication*, vol. 49, pp. 156-164.

Simon, H. (1955). "A Behavioral Model of Rational Choice." *Quarterly Journal of Economics*, vol. 69, pp. 99-118.

Simon, H. (1959). "Theories of Decision-Making in Economics and Behavioral Science." *American Economic Review*, vol. 49, pp. 253-283.

Simon, H. (1982). *Models of Bounded Rationality*. Cambridge, Massachussets: MIT Press.

Smith, M. D.; J. Bailey and E. Brynjolfsson (2000). "Understanding Digital Markets: Review and Assessment." in E. Brynjolfsson and B. Kahin, eds., *Understanding the Digital Economy: Data, Tools and Research*. Cambridge, Mass.: MIT Press.

Solow, R. M. (1956). "A Contribution to the Theory of Economic Growth." *Quarterly Journal of Economics*, vol.70, pp.65-94.

Stewart, J. (1995). *Language as Articulate Contact: Toward a Post-Semiotic Philosophy of Communication*. Albany: Suny Press.

Swan, T. W. (1956). "Economic Growth and Capital Accumulation." *Economic Record*, vol. 32, pp. 334-361.

Urbano, A. and J. Villa (2002). "Computational Complexity and Communication: Coordination in Two-Player Games." *Econometrica*, vol. 70, pp. 1893-1927.

van Ruler (1999). "De Dialoog als Methode". In *Kerk and Wereld*. Driebergen, the Netherlands.

van Siclen, C. W. (1997). "Information Entropy of Complex Structures." *Physical Review E*, vol. 56, pp. 5211-5215.

Vennix, J. A. M. (1996). *Group Model Building. Facilitating Team Leaning Using System Dynamics*. University of Nijmegen, the Netherlands.

Weiner, N. (1950). *The Human Use of Human Beings: Cybernetics and Society*. Garden City, NY: Doubleday Anchor.

INDEX

D

E

F

G

H

I

Q

R

S